The 2019 Anthology of Winning Irish Short Stories and Memories

THREE
SISTERS
PRESS

The *Ireland's Own* 2019 Anthology of Winning
Irish Short Stories and Memories

Editor: Phil Murphy

Production Editor: Michael Freeman

Advisory: Celestine Murphy and Liam Mulcahy

Published by: Three Sisters Press Ltd. Co. Wexford

Pre-Press and Printing by: W&G Baird

Distribution by: Gill Distribution, Hume Avenue, Park West, Dublin 12

© Copyright 2019, *Ireland's Own*, Channing House, Rowe Street, Wexford

ISBN: 978-1-9164494-4-2

WHAT THEY SAID ABOUT US ...

Quotes from the Forewords to our previous anthologies.

"IRELAND'S OWN HAS been like a good kindly Fairy Godmother for all of us, publishing our first works, giving us encouragement ... the magazine has been like a friend, a great cushion against the tough world out there."
– Maeve Binchy, 2010

"MY LINKS WITH *Ireland's Own* began in far-off days in my home town of Doneraile, Co. Cork, where I first encountered this fountain of stories, essays, jokes and Irishness in Titridge's shop. It has continued right through my life ... my last moments awake each night are spent reading the *Ireland's Own*."
– Donncha Ó Dúlaing, 2011

"I COMMEND *Ireland's Own* for their continued support and commitment to new Irish writers. Telling stories is in our lifeblood. The tradition of the seanachaí is ingrained in us and it is why we have so many wonderful writers in every genre."
– Patricia Scanlan, 2012

"HUGE THANKS TO the wonderful team at *Ireland's Own* for your continued support and encouragement to writers everywhere. You've no idea how much it means and long may your magical tradition of storytelling continue. It's a truly

amazing thing, actually seeing something you've written there in black and white taking its first baby steps out into the world."
– Claudia Carroll, 2013

"WHEN I HAD my first manuscript accepted by a publisher, I danced around the kitchen and sang 'Alleluia'. We writers have a deep desire to see our name [and our work] in print. This anthology provides that opportunity. Congratulations to all whose stories are glowing within."
– Alice Taylor, 2014

"THERE'S *IRELAND'S OWN*, one of the most widely read journals in this hemisphere, which mercifully provides outlets for all sorts of writing: from the comic to the ironic to the tragic, from reality to fiction … To know the magazine is still there is comforting to say the least."
– Billy Roche, 2015

"I AM DELIGHTED to be involved with the *Ireland's Own* annual anthology. Storytelling is something we do when we are grieving, or when we are full of joy … It is all storytelling. And it is what makes us human. *Ireland's Own* has been celebrating and encouraging the art of storytelling for over a century."
– Michael Harding, 2016

"FOR MANY EMIGRANTS, *Ireland's Own* is like a letter from home. So this year I will keep up the tradition and send these wonderful stories to New York. There's continuity in these pages, and a loyalty to both the reader and the writer that has passed the toughest test of all in publishing, and that is the test of time itself."
– Billy Keane, 2017

"I'M GENUINELY delighted to play a small part in the *Ireland's Own* anthology. In a country of writers and storytellers, *Ireland's Own* has long played an important role. It celebrates storytellers and offers a window into the lives of others. Long may it continue to do so."

– Rachel English, 2018

Introduction

IRELAND'S OWN, in conjunction with publishers Three Sisters Press, is very pleased to bring to readers our 10th anthology of the winners and other highly commended entries in the long-running annual writing competitions organised by the magazine.

This book is compiled from the 500 plus entries we received for our 2018 writing competitions and we are satisfied that the content is once again of a very good standard, indicative of the great writing talent out there.

Ireland's Own receives a great many submissions from our regular contributors every year, and we also receive a large number of unsolicited contributions every week, many of them of a good quality. We are only able to use a small portion of all these, but we do try to be encouraging and sympathetic in our approach as we are conscious of the great desire among people to get their work into print, and the small number of potential outlets available to them.

The anthology and our writing competitions are an essential part of our policy of encouragement and support. We thank former *Ireland's Own* editors, Gerry Breen, Margaret Galvin and Phil Murphy for their continued involvement with this worthwhile project.

We wish all the contributors future success if you continue to pursue your writing ambitions; *Ireland's Own* is very happy to have helped you take these first steps along the road.

The short stories and memories in this publication offer a good flavour of what is available every week in *Ireland's Own*, the publishing phenomenon that has continued without a break since 1902.

Our unique mix of entertaining, educational and informative features, song words, jokes, cookery, lifestyle and health, history and personal memoirs, also includes our old friends such as Cassidy, Miss

Flanagan and Dan Conway, and a substantial section specially for younger readers,

Even after 117 years the old maxim about Ireland's Own is as true as ever, *The Week Wouldn't Be The Same Without It*! And perhaps we can now say that the year would not be the same without the annual Ireland's Own Anthology of short stories and memories.

Sean Nolan, Editor, *Ireland's Own* and
Shea Tomkins, Assistant Editor, *Ireland's Own*

Contacting *Ireland's Own*

You can check out *Ireland's Own*, sample what we have to offer, take out subscriptions and air your views on our lively website at *www.irelandsown.ie*.

Phone us at 053 91 40140. If dialling from overseas, the number to ring is 00353 5391 40140.

Email articles to be considered for publication to: *submissions@ irelandsown.ie*

For general enquiries, email: *info@irelandsown.ie*

For subscriptions, email: *iosubs@irelandsown.ie*

You may write to us at *Ireland's Own*, Channing House, Rowe Street, Wexford, Ireland.

Editor's Note

AS A RETIRED editor of *Ireland's Own* I am very happy to maintain my association with the magazine as compiler and editor of the yearly anthologies and this year is something of a milestone as this is our 10th collection to be published.

I congratulate all those who appear in this year's production; quite a few regulars are again included, but others are being published in a book for the first time and their appearance in this volume will certainly mean a great deal to them, in particular. I thank all our writers for your help and co-operation and I hope you are happy with the end result.

The adjudicators assure me the standard has been very high once again and it should be a source of much satisfaction and pride to have made it between these covers.

The popularity of our writing competitions and the Anthology itself continues to grow and this volume contains entries from 14 Irish counties and various parts of the UK. As a matter of interest, Kildare is again the county with most entries at six, followed by Dublin with five and Wexford with four.

Well done also to the hundreds of others who entered our long-running annual writing competitions. I would certainly encourage you to stick with your writing; I am sure you will find it stimulating and personally rewarding and perhaps your turn will duly come in future anthologies.

A special word of thanks to Cathy Kelly, former journalist and international best-selling novelist since 1997, for contributing the foreword to this year's Anthology. She follows in a distinguished line of people who have endorsed our efforts over the years, including the late Maeve Binchy, Donnchadh Ó Dúlaing, Patricia Scanlan,

Claudia Carroll, Alice Taylor, Billy Roche, Michael Harding, Billy Keane and Rachael English.

My thanks to friends and former colleagues, *Ireland's Own* editors Sean Nolan and Shea Tomkins, for their ongoing help and support, and to the efficient *Ireland's Own* office staff who administer the competitions and book sales, and keep the wheels turning so well throughout the year.

I acknowledge the help and co-operation of Michael Freeman and all at Three Sisters Press, publishers of this edition of the *Ireland's Own Anthology of Winning Short Stories and Memories*, John Gibney, design consultant, and the many others involved behind the scenes.

Phil Murphy
August 2019

Foreword

By Cathy Kelly
International best-selling author

A MAGIC OCCURS WHEN a writer puts pen to paper, fingers to computer. It's a magic that comes from the determination to see if this dream is just a dream, or if it could be something more. Something magical.

Most of us spend years thinking about writing: storing ideas in our heads or in tattered notebooks, our lives full of 'if onlys'.

If only we didn't have work, we think.

If only dinner didn't have to be made.

If only we could escape the everyday parts of normal life, then we too would sit in luxury with a beautiful pen, pristine paper and great swathes of time in which to think.

Then, we could write.

However, the true magic of writing is never in a great swathe of time or of suddenly being relieved of all normal duties. No. The magic is in our hearts and souls because we have nurtured this belief that we have a story or a memory of times past inside us. One day, irrespective of making dinner or caring for our families or going out to work, the magic touch paper will be lit.

And we'll sit down to write. We dredge up the confidence from somewhere because fear stops so many of us from writing, and we start telling our story.

This anthology comes from a group of talented and brave people who stopped dreaming and let the magic of writing take over. They stopped worrying about being judged for their writing – and I am telling you, all writers worry about this.

They let the magic flow and I am thrilled to be the one to introduce this book and these writers to you, the readers.

Ireland's Own is part of the very fabric of our nation's rich cultural life. It speaks to and for people, and to write a story, or a long-held-onto memory, for the much-anticipated yearly anthology is a huge goal to aim for.

The wonderful writers in this anthology have done just that.

I am honoured to be involved merely by writing this introduction. I salute every one of you who is involved and say 'courage!' to those of you who'd love to do it but are so scared of doing so.

We are the land of the storytellers and we have it in our blood. Keep writing and enjoy this glorious anthology.

Cathy Kelly
September, 2019

CATHY KELLY is published around the world, with millions of copies of her books in print. A number 1 bestseller in the UK, Ireland and Australia, she is one of Ireland's best-loved storytellers. Brought up in Dublin, on leaving school she initially worked as a journalist with a national Irish newspaper. She juggled her job with writing in her spare time, and her first novel, Woman to Woman, *was published in 1997. It went straight to number 1 on the* Irish Times *and* Sunday Times *bestseller lists. Since then she has published almost 20 successful novels.*

Cathy's trademark is warm Irish story-telling about modern life, and her books deal with themes ranging from relationships and marriage to depression and loss, but always with an uplifting message, sense of community and strong female characters at the heart. She lives with her husband, John, their young twin sons, Dylan and Murray, and their three dogs in County Wicklow. She is also an Ambassador for Unicef Ireland, raising funds and awareness for children orphaned by or living with HIV/AIDS.

See Cathy's official website at www.cathykelly.com

CONTENTS

Competition Winners

Highly Commended

The Wake

By Maura Connolly,
Caragh, Co. Kildare

It is a sad day in the Kelly household as preparations are made, and friends and neighbours gather, to bid farewell to Bridget and Jack's beloved daughter, Mary.

BRIDGET KELLY SAT in the dappled shade of the apple tree behind the cottage. It was under that same old tree that she first saw love in Jack Kelly's eyes many years ago. To a passer-by she might seem an older lady but Bridget was only 42 years. The trials of life had taken their toll. Her strong, broad shoulders were burdened with bearing seven children, losing two sons to scarlet fever and Bridget Óg's weak chest was a worry, but nothing compared to how she felt today. 'My heart is broken,' she muttered as tears welled up in her eyes.

As she sat there, she saw Jack coming towards her. He took her in his arms and held her as she sobbed against his shoulder. Jack loved her so much and to him she was as beautiful as the first time he saw her. She wore a long grey skirt and white blouse which she had washed, starched and placed on the grass in the morning sun to bleach it. Then it was ironed with care. Her long blonde hair was streaked with grey and arranged in a bun on top of her head. Working outdoors feeding the animals and working on the bog had given her complexion a glowing tan.

An overwhelming feeling of grief swelled up in her heart, leaving her numb of all feelings. 'I must be strong' she said. 'Jack, I pressed your suit and I will wear my black skirt and shawl tonight. We must look our best for Mary. Last night I heard Bridget Óg crying in her sleep and calling Mary's name.' Memories of Mary's childhood flashed through her mind. 'Remember the day she was born, Jack. Your mother was so excited and I have no doubt she will look after her from her heavenly home. She was such a good child and she returned all the love we gave her.' Jack could not speak as he choked with sadness.

Mary was their eldest daughter and the apple of her mother's eye. Jack adored his beautiful daughter. She worked in the big house called 'The Hall' where she waited on the Lady of the house. The mistress was very fond of Mary and appreciated her hard work. She had a half day every Wednesday and she came home until next morning. Everyone looked forward to Wednesdays and Mary always brought a basket of food from The Hall kitchen as directed by the mistress. Bridget insisted that Mary lay down for a rest before tea as it was a two-mile walk from The Hall. Afterwards they would sit down to tea and there was always a treat from the basket. Bridget Óg loved to hear stories about life in the big house.

The Kellys had a good standard of living compared to many of their neighbours. They had a small farm and kept a cow and some pigs. Bridget looked after the hens and pigs. They sowed vegetables and had apple and pear trees, compliments of The Hall. Jack did odd jobs at The Hall and for extra small work he was often paid in kind. He was a generous man and helped his neighbours when possible.

Bridget walked slowly into the house and then into the bedroom. As she looked down on Mary her heart was breaking as she thought of the lonely Wednesday evenings without her.

Mary wore a green dress that covered her slim ankles. It was a dress too grand for a servant girl but it was given to her by her mistress and her mother had altered it to fit her elegant figure. She was a pretty girl with blonde hair and pale complexion, in contrast to Bridget.

She wore her hair in ringlets around her face. Mary would be 18 in two weeks and already had turned many a young man's head in the village and, indeed, of the young men who visited The Hall. She only had eyes for John MacGrath, son of the local blacksmith. It was hoped by both families that they would marry soon. Bridget had already started to make her dress and dreamed of her walking down the aisle with Bridget Óg as her bridesmaid.

'Oh, my darling child,' she cried. In spite of her overwhelming grief Bridget was aware of her blessings in being able to give Mary the send-off fitting for such a much loved girl. She was also conscious of her neighbours who had already shared her sorrow. A voice from the kitchen called out:

'Are you there Bridget?' She wiped away her tears and went to greet her neighbour and friend. 'A soda bread cake for tonight. How are you? I am here to help now,' Kate said all in one breath as she found it hard to find the right words. She was also sad as she knew Mary since she was a baby and having five boys and no girls, Mary often helped her with the boys when they were young. The two women hugged and cried for a few minutes. 'Bless you Kate, I don't know what I would do without you. You are a good friend and knowing I have you means a lot to me.'

'Now we will have a cup of tea and a piece of that fruit cake that Mrs. Smith from the shop left in this morning.'

'Aren't you honoured; are you sure it won't choke us,' remarked Kate trying to lighten the mood a little as Mag Smith was not known for her generosity.

But today her humour just fell flat.

The evening started quietly. The Rosary was recited and friends and neighbours began to arrive bringing with them small gifts of food or whatever else they could afford. Mrs Hamilton and her cook from The Hall arrived in the pony and trap bringing two big baskets of food. The poteen was stored in the hen house under the nests and covered with straw and a few eggs and it was safe there in case the excise man arrived.

Stories of the excise man, emigration, friends long departed, and hard times past and present that happened in their small village of Catheen were told and remembered. Tears flowed freely as Mary's life was recalled. She was a popular girl in the village, always ready to help friends and neighbours. Food was served, Mick McQuaid played his fiddle and then the dancing started.

Friends were invited to sing and when Kate sang *The Last Rose of Summer,* Bridget broke down in tears. Until then she did her duty, entertaining her guests in a quiet and dignified manner in spite of her fractured heart. When all had eaten and drank their fill it was late into the night and the visitors left after they said their goodbyes, good wishes and advice. Everyone agreed Mary had a great send-off.

Morning came too soon and John MacGrath arrived in his father's horse and trap to take Mary on the first part of her journey to Boston, U.S.A.

Maura Connolly lives in Caragh, with her husband Brendan. They have two sons, both living in Ireland. She worked as a nurse but is now retired. She started to write in 2009 and she is a regular contributor to Ireland's Own *magazine. In 2012 and 2016 her stories were Highly Commended in the Anthology. In 2017 she was shortlisted in the Newbridge June Fest Short Story Competition.*

The Bishop's Visit

By Margaret O'Doherty,
Raphoe, Co. Donegal

Recalling the pre-Confirmation visit to the school by the Bishop to question the candidates on their knowledge of the Cathechism, an occasion that led to an anxious frenzy of preparation and cleaning, for both the school and the pupils …

I WAS STILL IN Baby Infants when our school had its most important visitor. All the pupils of the single teacher school were in one room so even us little ones knew the bishop was coming. He wasn't coming to see us or ask us any questions but we would be there when the Confirmation class was subjected to the dreaded ecclesiastical exam.

At that time Confirmation was only held every three years, so children as young as nine had to undergo this ordeal. Each student had to answer one question and failure meant you could not be confirmed and you, your family and the whole school would suffer irredeemable disgrace. Nobody in our school had ever failed the exam. In fact, we didn't know anybody who had failed, which should have been encouraging odds, but there were dark tales of unfortunates forced to spend three extra years at school for the chance to face it again.

The bishop would conduct the exam according to a rigid but unwritten protocol. The most able students, always strategically placed in the front row, were asked difficult theological questions. For the dunces arrayed behind them there was a selection of easier questions like, 'Who made the world?' with the answer 'God made the world,' to ensure that all could make the grade.

Despite the near certainty of everyone passing, the students, parents and especially the teacher viewed the whole visit with trepidation. The school was scrubbed from top to bottom, no corner left untouched. The books, copies and globe that sat atop the large press set against the side wall were moved so that the biggest boys could pull it out. All the stuff lost behind it in the last three years was retrieved and the wall washed before it was pushed back in again. I wondered if the bishop was going to inspect behind the presses or between the floorboards as I joined in this cleaning frenzy.

Not only the building but the pupils had to be spotless for the visit. The night before I was bathed and had my hair washed. I always had a bath on a Saturday night with my younger sister so a midweek bath alone was a complete novelty. My best dress was washed and ironed, although I had never worn it. It had belonged to my cousin who only wore it on special occasions and had out-grown it after only a few outings so it was as good as new. To match it, my granny had cut a length of red ribbon almost as long as myself, cut a V shape at each end to prevent it fraying and ironed it to perfect smoothness.

The next morning I woke early. My mother scrubbed my face, neck and ears again in case they had got dirty in bed. New underwear was produced and then the special dress. Granny brushed my long blonde hair, combed it back from my face and tied it up with the ribbon made into a perfect bow as only she could. I looked like one of the Kennedy children in the magazines. The ribbon began to slide on the shiny, clean hair.

A multitude of hair grips were stuck in to keep it in place, each one drawing a yelp as it jabbed my skull but I was ordered to keep quiet.

My father drove us the short distance to the school so we would have no opportunity to get dirty marks on our new white socks. Nothing had been left to chance. We were all as close to perfection as humanly possible.

When the bishop arrived he wasn't as frightening as we expected. He was an elderly, rotund gentleman who looked like a granddad might if he dressed in black and wore a collar. He wasn't wearing a pointy hat and he didn't carry a staff but we were all afraid he might have it in the car and would get it if anybody deserved a belt of the crozier.

The bishop admired everything and said how good it was to see so many younger children at the school. The priest told him that the youngest pupil was the teacher's own daughter, sitting beside me at the very front, my sole companion in baby infants. The bishop came over to speak to us and immediately noticed my ribbon.

'That's a lovely red ribbon,' he said. 'Would you give it to me?' he asked in a tone only used for small children. I was too shy to answer but my more forward classmate piped up with an observation that left her mother's face as red as my ribbon. 'What do you want a ribbon for? You have no hair.'

Margaret O'Doherty is married with two grown-up daughters and works full-time as a pharmacist. She has been a member of The Diamond Writers group for about ten years and, thanks to their support and encouragement, has had several stories published, including one in the 2015 Ireland's Own Anthology.

The Lost Photograph

By Mary Burke,
Athgarvan, Co. Kildare

A missing family photograph has assumed great significance for Mary's dad as he nears the end of his days and she is delighted when it suddenly turns up. 'I never knew what she looked like until now,' was his simple but profound comment when he viewed it at last.

'SURELY SOMEONE MUST have it?' he enquired scratching his head, a trademark habit that he had when he was perplexed. I told him that I would do my best to see if I could locate the photograph. Everyone could tell me there was a photograph but where it was or who had it was anyone's guess. Then one Saturday morning in February a cousin called me and said that she had found the photograph in a press in the family home. It was with some other family memorabilia in an old biscuit tin.

'There was no frame, just the photo, yellowed and slightly frayed at the edges,' she said, as she handed me the large brown envelope.

'Mind it,' she said.

'I will to be sure,' I replied.

I couldn't believe my luck. I called him straight away and waited for him to pick up the phone. So many times, when I had called him, he would ask me again and again if I had any news on the whereabouts of the photograph.

'Well,' he said, 'any news?'

'I have it,' I said. 'It was found in an old tin box in a press in your brother's house.' There was silence at the other end of the phone. I waited for him to speak.

'When are you coming down?' he asked.

'Tomorrow morning, I'll see you around twelve o'clock after second Mass,' I said.

'I look forward to that,' he said.

When I put down the receiver, I picked up the envelope. I was tempted to open it but resisted. I placed it in my red satchel and left it at the front door. Next morning, I set off early for home. The morning sun drenched the countryside in a warm light as I drove along the winding country roads, listening to *Sunday Miscellany*. Several times throughout the journey I glanced across at the red satchel. I had thought about this moment so many times over the years and now it had finally come.

As I approached the house I could see him standing at the front gate, still dressed in his Sunday clothes, his collie dog, Sparky, sitting faithfully by his side. Usually after coming in from Mass he would change back into his working clothes and head for the fields. But today was different. He raised his right hand to salute me as I drove into the yard. I couldn't but notice his big hands, black and blue from all his years working at the sand and gravel business, loading and unloading sand and gravel off lorries with shovels. 'No machines back then,' he would always say.

I parked the car and took my red satchel from the back seat as he made his way down the yard towards me.

'Lovely morning, Dad,' I said.

'Yes, Mary, indeed it is,' he said.

'You have it with you?' he asked.

'Yes,' I said, pointing to the red satchel.

I walked along the path towards the house with him. The first shoots of green were everywhere to be seen and the crocuses and snowdrops were in full bloom.

'My favourite time of the year,' he said, as he gestured to the new growth.

'Mine too,' I replied.

'Your mother has been busy,' he said, pointing towards the upturned clay.

For the first time in a while I noticed how frail he had become, leaning heavily on the walking frame. My mother was waiting for us at the kitchen door.

'She's been baking again,' he said, gesturing to her flour-covered apron.

'I heard the car,' she said, rubbing her hands on her apron. 'He's been in and out to that front gate ever since we got home from Mass.'

We walked into the kitchen together and sat down at the large wooden kitchen table. My mother put the kettle on and we chatted about my journey down, the changes in the weather and the local news. She then made the tea and poured it into the willow-patterned cups, reserved for those special occasions. She took out the tray of scones from the oven and placed them on the table. Then she sat down beside my father.

Since I was a small child growing up he had always sat at the top of the table and my mother to his right. Today was different though as she moved her chair closer to his chair. She settled into the chair, folding her arms on the table, as if to indicate that all was now ready for me to proceed. I reached down into my red satchel and took out the brown envelope and placed it on the table in front of him.

'You didn't open it?' he enquired.

'No,' I said, 'it's yours to open.'

He stared at the envelope for a short while and then took it in his hands. My mother filled the silence with chatter about the new floral-patterned oilcloth which she had bought in the local hardware shop. The familiar kitchen sounds filled the silence, the gentle hum of the radio, the hissing of the kettle on the stove and the ticking of the clock. He lifted the seal on the envelope and took out the photo. We watched in silence as his eyes moved across the photo. My mother glanced anxiously in my direction. After a while he put the photo down on the table. We waited anxiously for him to speak. My mother reached over and gently turned the photo towards her and I moved my chair closer to hers.

'I never knew what she looked like until now,' he uttered in a low voice.

We stared at the woman in the photo, a round-faced, good-looking woman, with her hair tied back from her face. Sitting on a chair and carrying a baby in her arms, she was smiling and her eyes bore all the countenance of a jolly woman. Standing to her left was a girl with dark complexion and long black hair, clipped up with a white bow. There was a white-faced collie dog sitting just behind her. A tall girl with dark hair, dressed in a long black skirt and white blouse stood to her right. The woman's husband stood to the girl's left, with a boy of about nine years of age holding his hand.

Over the years we had heard the stories of fishing on Lough Bawn and so it was no surprise to see the fishing tackle hanging from the thatched roof of the farmhouse, providing the back-drop for the photo.

So, here was the woman he had longed to see, his mother, who had died when he was just a year and nine months. For

11

as long as I could remember he had talked about her. I leaned in and took a closer look to see if he resembled her in looks.

'You were called after her,' he said, looking over at me.

'I've always considered it a privilege to have her name,' I said.

'You have her eyes, Dad,' I said, holding back the tears. He didn't reply.

'Much too young to die,' my mother muttered, 'too young altogether, leaving seven small children.'

'That photo must have been taken around 1912?' I enquired. 'Bridie, Johnny and yourself hadn't been born then,' pointing to the four children in the photo. He didn't answer.

'You did good,' I said. 'And she would have been really proud of you.'

He got up from his chair, leaned heavily on his walking frame and headed out the back door towards the fields. I moved to follow him but my mother shook her head. I watched from the kitchen window as he ambled his way along the path and out through the red iron gate into the field. I watched until I saw him slump down onto the weathered wooden bench beside the cow shed.

'She was too young to die and he was too young to remember,' I said to my mother. She nodded in agreement.

In the weeks before he died we looked at that photograph several times. He recalled stories of fishing on Lough Bawn, growing up on the farm, stories of family, neighbours and friends from his home place and the legends of Lough Crew. I took a trip down to Lough Crew and then on to the site of his home place. I brought the photo with me.

I tried to visualise what it was like for him to grow up as a young boy in the 1920s and 1930s in this beautiful ancient setting in Co. Meath, without his mother. The deserted house and farm sheds, with their red galvanised roof sheets, now stood silent. As I turned to go I peered over the stone wall, which led from the house to the garden, and there lay the white carpet of snowdrops he had always talked about and remembered as a child growing up.

'Who's that woman standing at the door?' he asked my mother a few nights before he died.

'There's no one standing at the door,' my mother replied. But he insisted that there was a woman standing at the door. My mother eventually nodded by way of reassurance.

'The older generation believed that your own kin came to meet you at the end,' my mother whispered to me.

'Maybe that was his mother?' I asked but she didn't answer.

'Do you believe in an afterlife?' he asked me the next day, as I sat beside his bed.

'I don't know but I really do believe that we will all meet again,' I whispered, as if I had some deep spiritual insight. 'My friend tells me that we have to trust the blessed path.'

'It would be great to see her, just once,' he said. 'If only to hear her call my name.'

The night before he died we lit the tall white candle and placed it beside the photo on the table. I silently prayed that she would come for him and accompany him on his final journey. Shortly before he died he opened his eyes, turned to me and smiled.

Mary Burke is married with two adult children, recently retired and living in Athgarvan on the edge of the Curragh plains. In 2017/2018 she took a short story writing course with Kildare Writing Centre. 'While to date I have written and submitted a few stories to various competitions, this will be my first story to be published,' she said with a justified sense of pride.

Banshees and Buttermilk

By Patricia Carr,
Kindrum, Fanad, Co. Donegal

Mick's bones still shrank with shame at his cowardice. His harsh dry laugh in that moment of pretend disbelief still echoed in his soul. Mary's docile, tear-filled eyes did nothing to soften his attitude towards her predicament. Like most young men of the time in a similar situation, he tried shirking his responsibility …

'THAT AULD SHOP buttermilk has no taste,' Mick McFee muttered to himself. He sat back and closed his eyes. There it was again – that unearthly wail like a breath at the window. Ghostly and isolated, it wafted all around him. It floated forward and with sobbing sighs faded into the night beyond the hall door. Mick was on his own in the house with only the rustling of a mouse in the flake meal bin for company.

A gust of wind blew from the throat of the open chimney. Through the haze of curling smoke, grainy visions of their life together began to take shape in Mick's mind.

He could see himself waiting at the crossroads, wondering why Mary had asked him to meet her. His brief fling with Mary was only meant to arouse the jealousy of the real love of his life, and so win her back. In this he was driven out by the same wind when another lad stepped into the gap. At the junction he threw his old bike up against the briar hedge.

His sense of foreboding grew with the lengthening shadows. Time and again he tossed the gloomy prospect to the back of his mind. But as Mary straggled through the bushes, afraid of having been seen, he was left in no doubt. Her look of desperation was forever etched on his brain.

Mick's bones still shrank with shame at his cowardice. His harsh dry laugh in that moment of pretend disbelief still echoed in his soul. Mary's docile, tear-filled eyes did nothing to soften his attitude towards her predicament. Like most young men of the time, in a similar situation, Mick tried shirking his responsibility. Mary pleaded, almost begged him for his support. Her entreaties were dismissed as Mick, getting on his bike, called over his shoulder:

'Go home and have sense, you have nothing to get off me! It was up to you to watch yourself!'

Having said that, Mick abruptly turned, and without as much as a backward glance, left Mary severely alone. A mile down the road he pulled up. He sat on the grass verge and lit a Woodbine. By now some of the starch had run out of him. The die was cast. His name and, to a lesser extent, that of his family would be besmirched far beyond the boundaries of the parish.

Mick knew he would be a 'marked man' in the local dance hall. Even those girls who might have at one time pursued him would be reluctant to dance with him now. He would be classed as 'fast', a danger to a girl's reputation if she were seen in his company. Mick felt this so intensely that even the hills seemed to shy away from him, as he let himself in the back door. His footfall was heavy as he climbed the narrow staircase that led away into the darkness.

Mick tossed and turned that night. He could say nothing, pack his case and sneak off in the clouds of the night. But if he ran now, where would the journey end? His sudden disappearance would do nothing to pale the shadow that his actions had already cast on his parents and only brother. Horror stories he had heard about brutal gangers and measly landladies had him huddling further under the blanket.

It was a case of the boat or the farm – he would stick with the farm. Let the neighbours nudge and gawp. He was a scapegoat, totally blameless. That was Mick's story and he would stick to it.

The biggest challenge to this resolve came the next morning. Mick reasoned that it was best that he break the news himself rather than having his father and mother hear it second-hand. His breath froze with anxiety as he cleared his throat. Their reaction was less volatile than he had anticipated.

Mick's father's first suggestion was that Mick sue 'that girl' for slander. His mother, cutting in with her two pence worth, did not agree. Such a measure would be more effort than it was worth and would only arouse local interest. Their final word was to reassure Mick that nobody would lend any credence to his involvement, given his family's standing in the parish.

This mistaken belief was blown out of the water a few days later. As he returned from the fields Mick's path was blocked by three strapping men – Mary's father, Big John, and her two brothers.

'You marry my daughter or the Banshee will be wailing in earnest!' Big John roared.

Mick was left shivering in his shoes. It might have been a veiled threat but to Mick it was a serious ultimatum. Having exhausted his verbal manoeuvring skills in denial, he could feel two strong hands clutch at his throat. Big John demanded that Mick and Mary meet in his house the following evening at eight o'clock. In the interests of his own safety, Mick fell in with the plan and resumed his homeward journey.

A sheep dog ran to meet him, its tail wagging in welcome. Alerted by the barking, Mary's mother dashed out. Seeing Mick she gathered him into the house without a word of greeting. She proceeded to the chimney corner and there sat looking at him through the fingers with which she shielded her face. Big John, with a brief 'hello', drew a chair from underneath the kitchen table and beckoned Mick to sit down. John was a man who conducted his business with his back to the dresser. He cut to the chase, thus avoiding a long strange, interlude of agonising waiting.

'Are you denying that you are to blame? Are you calling my Mary a liar? What do you intend to do about this? Are you willing to marry her?'

The questions were rattled off as if they were being fired from a machine gun.

When he was challenged directly like this, Mick's own silence betrayed him. Mick noticed that Mary's opinion was not sought at all. She sat impassively, nodding in agreement to what, he was not sure. Whether or not she would consider marrying Mick if things were different, didn't come into it. Mick heard it said that the last key on the bundle can often open the lock. With this in mind, he finally spoke.

'Does Mary want to marry me?' he said. 'How could I support a wife and family – on eight shillings a day with my horse and cart on the Council? My mother is still hale and hearty and would not gladly allow another woman on her patch,' Mick said in a mealy mouthed way.

With this Big John's anger peaked. A well-aimed kick sent Mick's chair from under him and he found himself gazing up at Big John from the floor.

'For the last time are you going to marry her?'

Finding himself on eye-level with Big John's number ten hobnail boot, Mick could see that further denial was futile. Big

John conveyed him as far as the end of the lane. Then, with a hearty slap on the back, he said: 'Shake it Mick, you're a decent man after all!'

This grudging compliment did little to allay Mick's misgivings about the whole affair. Mary was a handsome girl but his parents' expectations for him were set much higher. He was not enamoured at having to marry in the teeth of family opposition. Nor had he anticipated how fierce the eruption of their anger would be. His father, pointing a finger in the direction of the door, reduced him to a quiver and finished him off with a bellowed remark.

'Get out!'

Mary's feelings or the welfare of their future grandchild were secondary to their reduction in social standing in the locality. His bones still shrank from the memory of that night and the events of the weeks that had followed. Mick was allowed back into the house, only to be ceremoniously escorted 'down to the room'. The priest sat at the oak table by the window. A whispered discussion followed. As he stood up to leave, the curate ran a finger under his Roman collar. Looking into the middle distance, he said thoughtfully:

'This will all blow by – you will still be one of our most respected families!'

This double-edged compliment cut Mick to the core.

The nuptials were arranged. Fr. White was curt and civil, but a bit peeved at having to open the chapel at the unearthly hour of two in the morning. While he waited, Mick could feel the damp of the hazy alcove settle on his Brylcreemed hair. A snarl of wood on wood as the chapel door opened let him know that Mary and her bridesmaid had arrived.

Mick turned to look at her in the liquid light of the candles. Pity was the only feeling for her in his soul. The thought of his unborn child was the silver lining in this cloud of doubt. As Mick signed the register, the scratch of the pen was audible in the silence. The wind in the rafters sang a joyless hymn as the small group left the church.

A misty rain was falling. Mick took off his coat, making a canopy over Mary. Mick linked arms with Mary. The night was dark, but the light of the hurricane lamp guided their steps along the narrow lane. The single end was just across the burn. Mick and Mary reached the gate. They moved through the gap into their new home, and the waiting years.

The walls were bare, except for a grocer's calendar. Furniture was sparse and the whitewash had long since turned yellow. Together they faced up to the challenge of building a life for themselves. Gradually Mick realised that he had landed himself a gem of a wife. Neighbours formed this opinion, too. Mary minded her own business. Yet, at the same time, hers was the first hand on the latch in a crisis. Mick licked his lips. He could still taste that homemade butter – and the tang of that butter-milk, fresh from Mary's churning.

Mick woke to the reality of the present. The house was hollow and cold without the woman who had threaded herself into his life for so long. Mick remembered, with a smile, the many times he sallied forth to Mary's old home, to beg for her return. She could be stubborn about it – but she always came back.

Mick drained the tetrapak. As he rose to shuffle towards the stairs, his legs gave way. He grappled with the seat of the chair in a vain attempt to raise himself. He felt faint. His surroundings swirled into one badly shaped blob. A low moan drifted from the street and curled itself over the half door. It closed in on him, he was ensnared in its clutches. A vision of Mary filled the room. There was something haunting, but celestial in her expression. She radiated a light into every corner, as if she was looking for someone. Her face was a bonfire of joy. Her presence enveloped Mick, ensnaring him in the brilliance of a summer cloud at sunset. Mary had once again come back.

Yawning in peaceful somnolence, Mick said resignedly:

'Take my hand, Mary. I could have left you for a life in exile. Thank God, I stood my ground. My life, our life, was here together. That life is over now, Mary – ending as it often played out – amid banshees and buttermilk!'

Patricia Carr is a native of Fanad, Co.Donegal, where she was born in 1947. Her first foray into writing was in the early seventies when she was a founder member of the Fanad Magazine Committee. She took up writing again after her retirement as school secretary in 2007. Last year, she helped set up 'The Four Seasons Writers', based in Milford. This small group have had three of its members published nationally to date. Fluent in Irish and widely travelled, Patricia is single and lives with her faithful dog, Hamish. This is her sixth appearance in the Ireland's Own Anthologies.

The Railway Station

BY VINCENT J. DOHERTY,
BURFORD GARDENS, LONDON

*The busy railway station was at the very heart of our town
during the 1950s, the theatre of dreams for many young people
where there was so much going on and so much to see, from the
joy of reunions to the sadness of departing emigrants …*

IF ONLY I COULD have driven a train, I would have been the happiest boy on God's green earth. Surely nobody could have had a greater ambition. Or, if I couldn't do that, I could at least lord it high up in the bell-jangling signal box, clanging the level crossing gates open and shut, handing out staffs promptly to train drivers as they powered their important way past, bringing the whole of Strabane to a halt.

The railway station was at the very heart of our town, a place to marvel at, trains you could set your watch by, mighty engines with hissing steam and screaming whistles arriving and departing clouded in smoke. It was our gateway to everywhere else. We were on the line to cities like Derry and Belfast and I remember an ancient sign to magical faraway places instructing travellers to 'Change for Letterkenny, Creeslough, Gweedore, Burtonport, Donegal, Stranorlar, Killybegs and Glenties.'

It was our theatre of dreams and, apart from the trains, it had the biggest clock I'd ever seen and a bookstall which, most importantly also sold *Beanos, Dandys* and bars of Five Boys chocolate. It was a place commanded by busy men in smart uniforms with brass buttons, where there was always something interesting to see, parcels and people and animals alike being loaded and unloaded willingly and unwillingly.

There were the business-like Great Northern trains arriving promptly with shuddering massive brakes and leaving with solemn whistles whilst quiet narrow-gauge Donegal Railway trains shunted and tooted modestly backwards and forwards among the sidings.

The station was a place of sorrowful partings and joyous reunions, of hugs and tears, often full of people on their way to earn a living somewhere else. There wasn't as much work as people thereabouts, so Strabane was a departure town with men and women from Donegal and farther into the West shambling off the narrow gauge carriages and mingling with the men and women from our town with all the enthusiasm of convicts ready to be transported.

They were waiting for the Great Northern to take them away on the Boat Train, a journey that would lead them eventually to lodging houses and employment in places like Cricklewood, Camden Town and wherever else Irish sweat was wanted, where, as Percy French put it, they would be '... digging for gold in the streets.' Families and friends would cluster on the platform to bid farewell to men in faded Sunday-best blue suits and tweed caps, lugging worn-looking brown cardboard suit-cases, many of them barely secured with string or binder twine.

'We'll be back for Christmas,' the emigrants would promise with lumps in their throats and tears in their eyes and, sure enough, some did return, if not for that Christmas for another one after that. I recall many a time in the days before the joyous festival, waiting for the Belfast train bringing my favourite Aunt Lizzie with a 'wee present' of a wooden train set or a regiment of lead soldiers as she returned from 'across the water'.

I remember too those summer mornings when the train from Derry brought our 'Scotchies', emigrants and the children of emigrants, bright eyed, full of anticipation coming 'home' for a lungful of Irish air and a fortnight away from their labours in the foundries, factories and laundries of Clydeside.

For one reason or another it was more than 40 years before I returned and by then the station was only a memory of old men who swore that as boys they'd seen Patrick Pearse passing them on a platform on his way to the Gaeltacht, and of old women who remembered Flann O'Brien getting off a train, coming back to visit his cousins, the Gormleys, in the town of his childhood.

The station and the trains had been there at the hub of everything for a hundred years but times were changing by the end of the 1950s and we were seeing the last days of the Donegal Railway and the Great Northern. They had survived after the War mainly by transporting workers to and from the linen mill at Sion or on the back of Orange and Green days like the Twelfth of July and the Fifteenth of August, and Bank Holiday excursions to seaside places like Bundoran. I remember our family waiting expectantly more than once with dozens of others dressed for a day in somewhere like Killybegs or Donegal Town.

But by the sixties the station would be abandoned to rust, the rails to weeds, and our Theatre of Dreams to the vandals who would wantonly destroy whatever might have been left.

Vincent Doherty was born in rural Tyrone during the last months of World War II but has lived in London for more than fifty years. He has always kept in touch with his Irish roots. He has spent most of his working life in education, teaching and working with young people nationally and inter-nationally, as well as teaching for some years within a goal kick of West Ham soccer club's ground. He also played a role with some young people in Britain's successful bid for the 2012 Olympic Games. He has appeared regularly in the Ireland's Own Anthology.

A Dramatic Introduction

By Madeline Breen,
Enniscorthy, Co. Wexford

*The influx of townspeople was giving a new lease of life to the
local village and the big annual community picnic was a great
place to meet the new neighbours and for them to be introduced to
local clubs and activities. All was going well until a drunken
loudmouth introduced some nasty racial abuse …*

THE AUGUST COMMUNITY picnic was the highlight of the parish calendar. Anyone new to the area
was encouraged to attend, to get to know their
neighbours and engage in local activities. At the picnic, local
book clubs, sports clubs, drama societies and charities found
lots of new recruits. It was always very well attended. Local
food businesses fell over themselves to cater at the event.

It had been Father Gordon's idea originally. He believed that
it was very important for a small village to develop a strong
community spirit. He had seen how in the towns, neighbours
no longer knew each other and wouldn't even know if someone
was sick or dying. He often preached from the pulpit of the
importance of looking in on neighbours who lived alone.
Not everyone appreciated his sentiments, as many of the
older people didn't want everyone poking their nose in their
business. Father Gordon's argument was that now they no
longer had a local GP, it was up to the community to check up
on those who were most vulnerable.

The influx of people from the town agreed with the priest for the most part. Many had moved from the town with their young families for a more wholesome lifestyle, away from the urban dangers. This brought large scale improvements to the school, due to extra funding, along with a number of new businesses run from home by tradespeople following the housing development that came with the migration from the town.

The local pub had no complaints, having once been near the brink of ruin. The recruits from the picnic for the soccer club had helped it avoid relegation and the drama society won its first big prizes since the sixties. New blood had brought new life to the village, thanks to Father Gordon's simple idea of bringing people together.

Lisa and Tony Mansini moved to the village where Lisa grew up four years ago and owned the Italian restaurant in town. The couple always supplied food for the picnic. Tony had a portable outdoor pizza oven and made the very best pizza outside of Naples. He also made *frizelle*, a dry, round bagel-type bread, to be dipped in cold water to soften. This could be topped with tomatoes, preserved grilled vegetables, herbs and cheese. This was a light alternative to the thick hamburgers, greasy southern fried chicken and spit-roasted pork that made up the rest of the culinary delights.

Lisa was opening another jar of grilled *melanzane* when she first saw the stranger. He was dark skinned, Middle-Eastern looking, with thick black hair, neatly slicked back and piercing dark eyes. He had a thick black beard, neatly trimmed, and walked shyly through the crowd clutching a bottle of diet Coke. Lisa felt sorry for him. In spite of his European clothing – a white Lacoste polo shirt and crisp blue jeans – he stood out from the largely Caucasian Irish gathering like the proverbial sore thumb.

'We should call him over here,' Lisa said to her husband. 'The poor man looks a bit overwhelmed.'

Tony nodded and looked to catch the stranger's eye. When the man looked over, Tony smiled and beckoned him to their stall. The stranger smiled back gratefully and nodded, and walked over to them. *'Ciao, senore!'* cried Tony. 'Welcome, welcome. Please, what can I get you?'

'Thank you, sir,' said the stranger with a slight bow of his head. 'I have always wanted to try Italian food. I believe that the Mediterranean diet is said to be one of the healthiest in the world.'

Tony beamed with national pride. He took a tray of pepperoni pizza and his pizza cutter and began to slice it up. 'Can I interest you in some of my country's national dish?'

The Middle-Easterner hesitated a little. Perhaps with just the cheese, if that's okay,' he said. 'I do not eat pork products. I am Muslim, you see.'

'Oh, of course, *perdona mi!'* said Tony, picking up a fresh cutting tool and moving to the tray of marghuerita. He sprinkled fresh basil leaves over a slice before passing it to the gentleman. The stranger took a bite, smiling as he savoured the burst of flavour from the sweet tomatoes, the faint tang of mozzarella and the pleasing aroma of the basil. Tony was pleased to see the stranger's nod of approval.

Lisa began to make conversation by asking the stranger where he came from. The stranger swallowed his pizza. 'I have come here from Pakistan, but I studied previously in London for a while,' he replied. 'I take it you are native to the village. How did you come to meet this Italian gentleman?'

Lisa chuckled. 'I was a Cullen, originally,' she explained. 'I met Tony when I was in Calabria, travelling after college. I got work teaching English and stuck around there for a bit. Tony's parents had a pizzeria where he worked and I would go for lunch. Eventually I ended up having lunch with him and his family in their home. We soon got married and after a few years, we came back here.'

The stranger nodded in understanding.

'So,' Lisa asked. 'How did you come to be in Ireland, and here of all places?'

The stranger was about to reply when Mick Callahan shouldered him aside, grabbing a slice of pepperoni pizza with his piggy hands. He staggered back and looked the stranger up and down with disdain. His face was red and shiny with sweat. His breathing was heavy. The stale smell of lager on him was unmistakeable.

'You watch where you're walking, Raghead'! growled Callahan, menacingly. 'Or I'll send you back to the cave you crawled out of!'

'Go home, Mick,' said Lisa sternly. 'You have had quite enough for one day.'

Mick turned to leer at her. 'Are you fed up with yer *Paesano* now, Lisa? Looking for a bit of Arabian Nights, hah?'

Tony stepped in beside his wife protectively but Mick then turned his attention to him. 'That's right, *Paesano*,' he sneered. 'None of her own are good enough for her. Now she fancies a bit of vindaloo.'

It took every ounce of restraint for Tony not to punch Mick's lights out, after that insult to his wife's honour. Father Gordon saw that Mick was looking to start something and tried to diffuse the situation. 'Here, Mick,' he called out to the drunk. 'Come over and have another burger, eh?'

Mick was undeterred and turned back to the stranger. Mick was a big, imposing man at six foot seven. Although the stranger was not short, he was certainly dwarfed by Mick's rugby player frame. Their noses nearly touched as Mick stared the Pakistani down. 'You're not wanted here,' he growled. 'Go blow yerself up somewhere else.'

A crowd was beginning to form around them, sensing a fight was about to occur. The only sounds to be heard were a sizzling hamburger and Mick's bull-like breathing. The stranger was thoroughly embarrassed at the scene he was now the centre of. The Mansinis were embarrassed too, that one in their own village could be such a bigot.

Even still, the stranger stood his ground calmly. He was about to tell the drunk he did not wish to make any trouble, when the hulking bully suddenly collapsed before him in a heap. Mick's pizza slice fell meat side down on the grass.

Someone in the crowd screamed, but the Pakistani sprang into action. He turned Mick onto his back and leaned over him to listen to his breathing. It was shallow and laboured. The stranger looked to the Mansinis, who stood next to him, stunned. 'Call an ambulance, please and quickly,' he said. Lisa took out her phone and dialled. Meanwhile, Tony called for the curious onlookers to stand back. The Muslim undid Mick's shirt and removed his chain and wristwatch. Seeing this as suspicious behaviour, Father Gordon jumped to conclusions and grabbed the stranger's shoulder.

'What do you think you're doing?' demanded the priest, angrily. The Muslim turned calmly to him.

'Where is the nearest defibrillator, Father?' he asked. The priest was momentarily confused by this reply. The Pakistani looked Father Gordon dead in the eye. 'Father,' he said, this man is having a heart attack. He needs treatment fast. I removed the metal from him to prevent interference when a shock is administered.' He placed the chain and watch in the priest's hand. 'Now again, where is the defibrillator?'

'In-in the parish hall,' stammered the priest. The Muslim asked him to go and get it, and to hurry. Tony went with him. The Pakistani turned back to the patient and began chest compressions. As he did so, the Pakistani looked at Lisa. 'Where can we find something to shave the chest hair?' he asked. Mick's chest was covered in thick black hair. 'We need to shave the hair to prevent interference with the current when the shock is administered. If the pads are not in direct contact with the skin, the shock will not work properly.'

A lady in the crowd of onlookers piped up. 'I have a brow trimmer here,' she said. Rummaging through her handbag, the lady produced a pen-sized device, the kind of which was advertised on TV for removing unwanted facial hairs. She stepped forward to hand it to the Pakistani. He smiled and thanked the lady, handing the trimmer to Lisa. He instructed Lisa to trim the chest hair from Mick's right pectoral and under his ribs on the left. As Lisa was doing this, Tony came back with Father Gordon, carrying the defibrillator pack.

The Muslim took the pack from them and fired it up. A robotic voice issued instructions to remove the pads from the pack. Using a tissue, Lisa wiped clean Mick's chest of stray hairs and sweat. The Muslim peeled off the sticky covering from the pads and attached them firmly to the shaved skin. Checking to ensure that the wires were correctly attached, he ordered everyone to keep clear, moving back from the patient. A light on the defibrillator pack turned green and the Muslim administered the charge.

Mick's body jerked as the shock went through his body. There was tense silence, as the crowd waited for the defibrillator to check for a steady pulse. It seemed as though everyone present was holding their breath. Mick groaned as the robotic voice from the pack confirmed the charge was successful.

There was a round of applause for the Muslim who had brought the bigoted man back from the brink of death. Men clapped him on the back and ladies shook his hand exclaiming how brave and calm he was in a crisis, how they would never have known what to do if it had been them. Some women probably even had the fleeting thought about whether he might be single.

Father Gordon sighed with relief as the pads were removed from Mick's chest. He silently thanked God. But he also had someone earthly to thank for saving his parishioner's life, and to apologise to.

The priest took the Pakistani's hand and shook it firmly. 'I owe you an apology,' he said. 'Before, I let my prejudice get the better of me and for that, I am ashamed. Thank you for saving Mick's life, in spite of how he spoke to you. It was a very noble thing to do.'

'Apology accepted, Father,' said the Muslim smiling. 'As for this man, I was only doing my job.' The priest looked at him quizzically. 'Allow me to introduce myself. My name is Dr Devendra Yusef. I am the new local GP.'

Madeline Breen has been writing stories, plays and even comics from a very young age. She holds a Joint Honours BA in Drama and Theatre Studies and English from University College Cork. She has recently resurrected her love of writing and was shortlisted for the WexWorlds Short Story Competition 2018. She has a blog called 'The Book Junkie' *and has guest written for the blog,* 'Between My Lines', *covering the 2018 Readers and Writers Day at the Wexford Literary Festival. Madeline lives in Enniscorthy with her pet cockatiel, Lady Gaga. She is working on her first novel.*

A Raw Night in Ballyragget

By Chris Lawlor,
Dunlavin, Co. Wicklow

Kit Kirwan had a lot of time for his older cousin Molly as he was growing up; she was a real livewire, involved in everything that was going on in the parish, and a source of some awe and inspiration to him. He kept up to date with events in her life though he had not met her since her wedding, but he was here to see her now …

THERE WAS A LONG line of people outside Ballyragget community hall. Kit Kirwan nipped across the road and joined the back of the queue, bowing his head and stooping slightly to try to get some shelter from the elements in the lee of the young man directly in front of him. Those elements were going at it hammer and tongs. The Arctic Circle, which he had been studying recently in geography, came into nineteen-year-old Kit's mind.

Sheets of sleety rain fell steadily. The wind howled around the assembled crowd, so the sleet was hitting them at a near forty-five-degree angle. It was a night fit for neither man nor beast. Kit heard someone a bit ahead of him in the queue allude to this fact when she said, 'You wouldn't put a dog abroad on a night like this.' Kit huddled deeper into his coat, thrusting his cold hands further into the pockets as he waited. 'It won't be long now,' he told himself. 'I'll see her again very soon.'

The girl in question was called Molly and she was Kit's cousin. As a child he had often visited her home, a farm in Knockbawn on the road between Castlecomer and Ballyragget. Her father, Kit's Uncle Mick, was his mother's brother. He was big, broad-shouldered and brawny and he always had a great welcome for Kit and his parents.

Kit remembered him best ankle deep in rich brown clay, standing in wellington boots atop the ridge which marked the highest point of his farm, like a lord surveying his manor, regaling his young nephew with stories of the old times. 'This was the place where my father hid from the Black and Tans, Kit. He lay down all day in the potato drills and your mother – she was only a little girl at the time – brought him milk and bread even though the Tans were parked up in the yard below. Did you know…?'

'Now Daddy, don't be boring Kit with those tall tales. Would you like some lemonade Kit? Come away into the house.' Great as Uncle Mick's welcome was, Molly's trumped it.

Molly was seven years older than Kit and he saw her as a bit of a heroine when he was growing up. He still couldn't decide whether he had a secret crush on her, but he knew that he never met anyone more alive. At the age of ten or eleven he noticed that Molly was always planning something when he visited. She'd often pay just a flying visit into Knockbawn, grabbing a sandwich or a few scones before rushing out to some event or other.

She was involved in many different organisations and her exotic pursuits such as the Macra quiz night, the drama group's play or the parish social fuelled the imagination of a young lad like Kit. Her mother, Auntie Mary, who was always busily bustling around the house and looking after Mick and all the children, maintained that any event 'wouldn't be held without Molly' and Uncle Mick swore that 'if there was a dogfight in Clogh, Molly would be at it.' In all her comings and goings though, she always had a kind word for the tongue-tied young cousin down visiting the farm.

'Sorry!' The woman behind Kit had inadvertently stepped on his foot, interrupting his train of thought. The queue was moving slowly, but the rain was coming down in bucketfuls, and the biting wind cut him to the bone. He knew the people would move inexorably into the hall and he knew he'd see Molly again for the first time in four years or so, but it wouldn't happen before he was thoroughly soaked.

Kit thought about lighting his pipe; he had taken up smoking it at university because he thought it lent him an air of gravitas, but he gave up on the idea almost immediately. In this rain the bowl would fill with water and there was no hope of striking a match in the gale that was blowing. He resigned himself to being cold, wet and smokeless, but a chink of light came into his world when he noticed that he was now only a few yards from the door. Two girls in their twenties were silhouetted in oncoming headlights as they dashed across the road to join the queue behind Kit. Something about the movement of one of them, a kind of shrug, reminded him of Molly again.

Movement was synonymous with Molly in Kit's consciousness. As well as being thoroughly alive, she was also a very lively girl. He had never met anyone more vivacious. She'd run or skip around the place doing her jobs in the fields and the farmyard, and she'd always be dancing around the house to the music of her tiny transistor radio. She it was who introduced Kit to Radio Luxembourg!

As he entered his teenage years, she entered her twenties and she was still dancing, but now mostly in the night clubs in Kilkenny and more and more with a young man called Paddy Comerford. Kit knew that Molly had a procession of boyfriends over the years, though details were scant as they were never discussed in his presence.

However, it was soon apparent even to him that Paddy was the one. They were married in Castlecomer church when he was fifteen and Molly moved into Ballyragget with her new husband. Kit gave them a condiment set as a wedding present – to him, Molly was always the salt of the earth.

Kit hadn't seen Molly since her wedding. He was at the awkward teenage stage and didn't want to accompany his parents on their visits to his Uncle Mick and Auntie Mary. They kept him informed about events in County Kilkenny though, and he knew Molly had three children in fairly quick succession. He finished secondary school and went on to university in Dublin, managing to scrape through the exams despite having a ball in first year.

He was old enough to frequent night clubs and dance halls himself now that he was in his third month of second year, and he was mightily relieved when the slow-moving queue at last moved inside Ballyragget hall. The change in temperature was immediately apparent and very welcome, as an electric wall-heater did its job. Steam began to rise from his saturated clothes. With the rain no longer beating against it, Kit lifted his face and looked expectantly ahead.

He blinked a little, adjusting to the light in the entrance area. It was poorly lit, but bright after the darkness of the cold, wet, bleak November night. The noise level had risen significantly, with all the sounds inside the hall reverberating and echoing off the walls around him. He always associated halls like this with Molly. These were the mysterious places to which she'd disappear, leaving her younger cousin in Knockbawn with the older generation.

She spent a lot of time in these halls, dancing, singing, acting, quizzing and generally socialising. She'd also spend a lot of time getting ready to come to these places: the mysteries of makeup and of choosing clothes for the occasion were somewhat lost on Kit, but even he knew that these things took a lot of time and effort and were important in her busy, whirlwind life. He continued to look ahead as he moved forward into the main hall.

Then he caught his first glimpse of her. Yes, there she was, and looking very well, he thought. Her long dark tresses were impeccably combed back and her kind face glowed beneath a sheen of makeup. Both the kindness and the glow were accentuated by the fact that she wasn't wearing her glasses. She had the longest eyelashes he'd ever seen on anyone. Her earrings sparkled in the lights and her pale pink lipstick matched the colour of the top she was wearing. And as always, she was fashionably dressed.

It had been a while since they met, and she was surrounded by other people, but Kit moved forward resolutely. Seeing her now at the centre of a cluster of people brought back more memories. He thought of her lively disposition, so obvious at past meetings. He thought of her kindness at including her younger cousin in all the hurly-burly of her life in the fast lane. He thought of her hearty greetings at previous meetings and remembered how her firm handshake had nearly hurt his young hand on more than one occasion.

The moment had come. Kit was now directly opposite her, looking into her face. He stretched out his hand and grasped the sprig of yew. He shook some of the holy water off it and sprinkled the remainder over Molly's lifeless corpse. He bent over and kissed her cold forehead, as he touched her stiff and clenched hand. The rosary beads she held was dark against the pink of her blouse. As he moved slowly around the coffin he looked into the bemused face of Uncle Mick and the broken face of Auntie Mary. As his own tears welled up, he managed to tell them how sorry he was, stuttering and stammering in his confusion and sorrow.

'I know Kit. Thanks boy.' Uncle Mick, his broad shoulders sagging under the weight of the world, nonetheless looking him squarely in the eye. 'Molly always had great time for you.'

Auntie Mary's response was a little more mechanical. 'Aren't you great to come?' she asked rhetorically, before lapsing into a disconcerting silence again.

Her eldest son, PJ, stood beside her. He was thirty years of age and he simply observed 'This is a hard one boy. Death is all very fine until it comes to your own door.'

Kit muttered a reply and passed on to the rest of his cousins, shaking each one by the hand and sympathising with them, before coming to Paddy and his three infant orphans. A widower at twenty-nine, with the weight of the world on his shoulders and suffering evident in every line of his face, he was literally in a daze. Kit whispered 'So sorry' and moved on.

Kit met his mother and father in the outer room. They were speaking in hushed tones with other relatives. He'd been away at college and had come down to Ballyragget on the bus, so he only knew that the cousin who had always been so alive was suddenly dead. He found out the cause of Molly's demise in that little room. It transpired that she contracted a kidney infection and was either too embarrassed or too busy (or both) to get it treated. By the time she collapsed, it was too late.

As he sipped his tea, Kit studiously avoided eye contact with everyone else in the group. He looked up at a cobweb in the corner of the ceiling. He looked down at a crack in the floor. He looked back into the room where Molly's coffin rested. It was beyond comprehension. An hour later, Kit braced himself at the front door of the hall, looking out into the freezing wind and the sleet which was falling heavier than ever.

Though he was now a university man and all of nineteen years old, Kit felt alone and very vulnerable. It was his first experience of a young person's death. The thought that 'she was my generation, only my generation' kept going around and around in his pounding head. He faced into the journey ahead dumbfounded, disbelieving and deeply depressed. Well might the heavens weep. He stepped outside… it was indeed a raw night in Ballyragget.

Chris Lawlor is a retired secondary school teacher living in Dunlavin, Co. Wicklow. He is married to Margaret and they have three sons, Declan, Jason and Michael. He has published ten history books and many historical articles and essays in journals, magazines and anthologies. Chris won the Dunlavin Festival of Arts short story award in 2001 and is a member of the Dunlavin Writers' Group.

The Sunday Game

By Liam Cahalan,
Aughboy, Clonlara, Co. Clare

*There was a 'Sunday Game' in rural Ireland long before
the popular RTÉ television GAA highlights programme
hit the airwaves forty years ago. The weekly card games
played in neighbours' houses, and all the little rituals
attached, were part of the social fabric ...*

THE THREE OF them are small, hardy men, with faces
burned from exposure to wind and sun and deeply lined
from hardship and long years of toil in the fields of north
Tipperary. Lifelong bachelors, they are quiet and taciturn, and
when in each other's company need few words to communicate.
They are good neighbours, always ready to give a day in the bog
or with the hay, or help pull a bullock from a drain of a summer
evening. Sound men.

On winter Sunday nights they come to the house, each within a
few minutes of the other. A creak of the gate, a pause to prop the
bicycle against the wall by the road. The soft knock at the door, a
lift of the latch.

'God save all here.'

Voices young and old respond.

'Goodnight, Danny.'

Danny is usually first of the three, coming in from the darkened
yard, clad in a heavy winter coat and flat cap, bicycle clips in one
hand and a lamp in the other. He carefully stores the lamp, a foul-

smelling relic operated by a lump of carbide, on the top of the dresser, and puts the clips in the pocket of his coat before hanging it on the back of the door. He greets the assembled family, and takes his place at the kitchen table, pipe, matches, tobacco and knife in position, near to hand.

The big rectangular table is empty and spotless, save for a deck of well-used playing cards.

Tom is next to come in from the darkness, similarly clad in coat and cap, his Sunday trousers tucked into his heavy winter socks, his bicycle lamp, a modern battery-operated model. He removes his coat, takes his place at the table, and also sets his pipe smoking paraphernalia in front of him. Both men busy themselves cleaning, filling, tamping down and lighting their pipes, wafting a thick cloud of aromatic smoke upwards into the yellow light of the softly hissing Tilley lamp. Their caps are not removed.

Pat, usually last of the three, arrives, clad for the cold and damp, coated and capped, lampless, but armed with a bag of acid drops for the young spectators around the kitchen. The woman of the house takes charge of the sweets, Pat takes his spot at the table, greets the others, a pack of Woodbines and matches set before him, and adjusts his cap into the playing position.

The host moves to his place at the table, laying down a packet of Players Navy Cut and matches. A quick step up on his chair, gives the Tilley hanging from the rafters a couple of pumps. The light intensifies, the hissing grows louder, and the game begins.

The cards are counted, the jokers discarded, the deck boxed and cut. The click and snap of the cards in the dealer's hands counterpoint the soft hissing of the lamp, and the rustle of the Sunday paper from the woman's chair by the fire.

The watching children are silent. The cards, thirteen to each, are gathered into calloused hands, fanned out, sorted into suits, trumps on the left, from best to least. Two cigarettes add to the miasma of smoke hanging over the table, and the player immediately left of the dealer leads off.

Concentration is total. The four, three still be-capped and one hatless, play in complete silence. Not a word is spoken. Cards played, tricks gathered and stored in front of the winner, the little stacks of four cards neatly placed in a row, one at right angles to the next.

Thirteen cards are played from each hand, thirteen leads, pauses for contemplation, thirteen tricks completed. Then a short post mortem, possible errors and soft tricks pointed out, the deck regathered and boxed, the score passed on to a watching child to remember. Hunched to the table, eyes narrowed in concentration, or possibly against the smoke, the game continues.

The host runs his hand through his luxuriant hair from time to time. A rasp of a striking match, the flip of the falling cards and the hissing Tilley background the tension. The magic number of twenty-six tricks is achieved. They relax, sit back, congratulate the victor, and three silver sixpenny pieces are handed over, to be stacked next to his smoking paraphernalia. On they go.

There is a stir as the woman of the house rises from her chair by the fire.

'Ye'll have tea.'

The cards are cleared, mugs of tea and slices of homemade curranny cake appear and are consumed with great thanks and compliments. A hum of conversation rises, talk of school, hurling, fishing. Deaths and marriages. Price of cattle. The weather. The table cleared again, the children ushered off to bed, and the game resumes and continues into the night.

Later, from my snug bed, I can hear my father in the yard with the three men, the rumble of the male voices in the quiet night as they wheel their bicycles onto the road.

'Goodnight, God bless, and safe home.'

The creak of the closing gate.

The three, caps low, trousers tucked and clipped, mount their bicycles and pedal steadily away into the silent winter night.

Liam Cahalan is retired about five years now. Originally from North Tipperary, he now lives in lovely East Clare. Married to Deirdre, they have four adult children, and three grandchildren. He has been writing on and off since he retired, and has been lucky enough to win the Memories section of the Ireland's Own *Writing Competition once, and was runner-up on two occasions. He has had about a half dozen memories pieces published in the* Ireland's Own *magazine. He is a keen hill walker, and plays the guitar and the concertina.*

Death, the Leveller

By Marion Fenton,
Doonass, Co. Clare

*The late Paddy Finnigan has had a long and ultimately losing
battle with alcohol and now his former wife, his very few friends
and some acquaintances have gathered to bid him a final
farewell and to reflect on his life and times …*

IN A SMALL TIPPERARY town in late November '65,
an icy wind blows as the hearse slowly approaches. A coffin
of cheap pine carries Paddy's remains towards the church
gate. His ex-wife, Annie, looks bereft, a black mantilla obscures
her face. 'God help me get through this day,' she mutters under
her breath. 'Thank God that the clergy agreed to bury him on
consecrated ground.' Her mind keeps flitting from one thought
to another.

Kitty, her only sister, links her in a gesture of support. 'C'mon
Annie, you're great to be here at all, a pauper's funeral is what
he deserves.'

This is of little comfort to Annie but at least Kitty's physical
presence helps on this perishing cold morning. There is no sign
of their son, Martin; she had fervently hoped that he might
turn up today.

Back in the day when she first met him, Paddy was six foot
tall with jet black hair and a confident swagger. He had a good
job, you'd hear him whistling before you'd see him, cycling to
work on the railway. He used to sing *Slievenamon* and Annie
adored his deep rich voice. She could not believe her luck

when he singled her out for a date. Love quickly blossomed and they were married in late September 1946.

They settled into a nice terraced house on Station Road and they were very happy. Annie fell pregnant the following year and Paddy took on a few gigs to earn extra money. He was out late singing over the weekends, she remembered the smell of drink as he climbed into bed beside her. She didn't mind as she felt he deserved a pint to unwind.

Following a difficult forceps delivery, their son Martin was born. She was very depressed and for some unknown reason Paddy went on a drinking binge. There was no talking to him during this episode. Full of remorse afterwards, he became a model father and husband, promising her faithfully he'd never touch a drop again. He gave up the singing and joined the Vincent de Paul. Often times he was seen carrying food supplies and clothes to the poor of the town.

All went well for a time until she found his pioneer pin at the back of his lapel and knew he was drinking again. He truly meant to quit but alas some innate weakness would overwhelm him and the cycle would start all over again. His mother, Doris, didn't help either; she'd call when Annie was out and say:

'Go out for a pint Paddy and I'll mind the little lad.'

Paddy would meekly do as he was told. Despite her anger, Annie held her tongue until finally she had a blazing row with Doris.

'How dare you tell your poor pet Paddy to go for a pint, he's a bloody alcoholic for Christ sake; get out of this house and don't come back.'

This caused ructions for a time, and Paddy's response was to go on another bender. Despite everything, Annie loved him and really tried to control his drinking. She coaxed him to attend AA meetings and he got a sponsor to support him. Annie went to Al Anon. They learned the twelve steps and used to recite them together – *'Powerless over alcohol, a belief in a power greater than ourselves, when wrong promptly admit it.'*

During his dry periods they had great times together. She remembers him laughing and kicking a ball with Martin in the backyard, or splashing about in the sea in Tramore with Martin high on his shoulders, shrieking with delight.

When Martin hit puberty he really struggled with his father's erratic behaviour. His school work was suffering and he hated his pals seeing his father legless around the town. Annie was torn; despite her love for Paddy she ultimately realised she was fighting a losing battle and separated from him. Her deep faith helped her to cope through this difficult period.

Paddy moved in with his mother who suffered a stroke and was dead within the year. Paddy was heartbroken and despite Annie's ongoing support, his life slowly descended into a downward spiral of drinking.

Annie shakes hands with the few mourners present at the funeral. There's a well-dressed chap from the Vincent de Paul, two AA members who had come to pay their respects and a man from the railway is present. Two destitute men with shoulders hunched are in attendance. She knows poor Jimmy, who is unshaven and with the fetid smell of dank clothing and stale whiskey on his breath.

He grew up in a reform school in Cashel where he was bullied mercilessly. Alcohol helped him to escape to a place where life was more bearable for him. At least he came to bid his pal farewell. Annie chats to Ned, who has made a supreme effort to scrub up this morning, even rubbing brylcreem on his unruly hair to honour his friend's passing. He stubs out his fag on the gravel and sprinkles holy water on his forehead.

Ned's child drowned while out fishing with him. He never got over it and lost his wife and a hundred acre farm to drink. The late Paddy and Ned were thick as thieves, they shared his mother's house – now gone to rack and ruin. They looked out for one another as best they could.

Just a few days previously, Ned found Paddy burning up with jaundiced skin in a laneway in the town. He couldn't rouse him and rang the ambulance. He was diagnosed with late stage cirrhosis of the liver and he died before Annie made it to the hospital. He was due to turn forty that same week.

Ned is cut up and struggling to stay sober till after the burial. He sympathises with Annie saying:

'Thank you for giving him a decent send off.'

Her sister Kitty acknowledges Ned but is reluctant to shake hands with Jimmy, as if the poverty was contagious and could be passed on by mere touch.

Father O'Hara readies himself in the sacristy beforehand. He looks in the mirror admiringly at his rich ivory/green robe emblazoned with a gold cross on his chest. A cream, embossed biretta with four commanding horns completes his regalia. Regardless of his attire, he's not happy to be here.

'Where is the curate who should be conducting this façade?' Father O's thoughts are giving him a headache and he rubs his temple to ease the pressure. Nevertheless, as he steps outside, his self-assured demeanour and his powerful voice contrasts sharply with that of the few grim mourners. He sympathises with Annie, enquiring about her son Martin. Jimmy hides behind the pier ashamed of his very presence here. As the priest ushers all into the church, the sound of a murder of cawing crows seems a fitting musical accompaniment.

The mourners fill the top two pews of the otherwise empty church. Last Sunday's drooping flowers add a smidgen of colour to the altar. The women bow their heads and clutch their rosary beads. The two boyos grip their caps and hope it'll all be over soon. The heat is on in the church but it fails to add a modicum of comfort to the icy atmosphere. Celebrating the sacrifice of the Mass was considered unnecessary as the deceased was a non-believer and therefore a short funeral service would have been acceptable to all.

Father O'Hara welcomes the mourners. Behind him the beautiful multi-coloured stain glass window depicting 'The Poor Man's Bible' seems an appropriate adornment. The candles are lit by the altar boys who proceed to hold the thurible open to enable Father O to place the incense inside. It is suspended from chains as he swings it to keep the incense burning. The smell provides a kind of comfort and solace to the small congregation.

Father O throws holy water on the coffin and blesses the holy soul of Paddy Finnigan. His brief homily includes remembering the young Paddy, cycling with his son on the bar of the bike, a pleasant sort of fellow, always ready to do someone a good turn. He concludes with 'Unfortunately the demon drink took hold of Paddy in later life.'

He goes on to warn of 'The destruction of the flesh and the torment awaiting the unrepentant sinner.'

The two lads would like the ground to open up and swallow them but thankfully the priest moves on. He asks for God's forgiveness on behalf of the deceased. He blesses the coffin and prays 'Holy Mary Mother of God, pray for us now and at the hour of our death. Amen.'

Finally it's coming to a close. 'May perpetual light shine upon him, may he rest in peace. Amen.' All make the sign of the cross as they depart from the church. Jimmy is in bad shape and disappears for a snifter to steady his fraying nerves.

The coffin is carried by the funeral director, two AA men and Ned who insists on carrying his friend to his final resting place.

Annie's lone floral tribute of fresh lilies adorns the coffin and adds a sweet aroma.

The church bell tolls as they walk slowly towards the freshly dug grave. Father O quickly completes the funeral ceremony 'May his soul, and the souls of all the faithful departed, through the mercy of God, rest in peace. Amen.'

All present bless themselves at the graveside as the coffin is lowered down. The men shovel icy earth on top of the coffin as the wind howls, biting into their freezing bones. Father O quickly takes his leave and the mourners are relieved when he is gone.

In the distance Martin can be seen running along. Annie is delighted to see him and shouts 'Better late than never son.' She warmly shakes his hand.

'Sorry Mam, the bus broke down and I had to thumb a lift.'

'No worries son, I'm happy you're here now.'

She links him as she draws him into the small congregation. Martin is training to be a technician with Eircom in Cork. He's here for his mother's sake only, having cut off from his father some time ago.

Ned is clearly moved to do or say something. He hesitates, Annie notices and gives him the encouragement he needs. He clears his throat to say a few words.

'Today, we say goodbye to Paddy, we thank him for being the unique character that he was, for the great songs he sang and for being a good friend to me during tough times.'

He takes a dirty piece of paper from his pocket, and in a proud voice sings a song for his friend.

> *'I'll sing you a song of the world and its ways.*
> *And the many strange people you meet,*
> *From the rich man who's rolled in his millions of wealth,*
> *To the struggling poor wretch on the street.*

> *But a man tho' he's poor, and in tatters and rags,*
> *We should never affect to despise,*
> *But think of the adage, remember my friends,*
> *That six feet of earth makes us all of one size'*

(K. W. Helmick 1878).

He concludes with:

> *'Today Paddy joins his mother in the earth – that great leveller*
> *of life.'*

Ned, in his love for his friend, gives him a dignified send-off which captures the essence of Paddy and of all our humanity. His song moved the mourners in a very profound way. They huddle closer together reminiscing about Paddy's life. Even poor Jimmy feels part of this. He tells a yarn of his own. They talk about Paddy's work with the Vincent de Paul and how he loved to help people when he could.

Annie is pleased her son is listening to this. She thinks perhaps in time he will see that his father wasn't all bad.

Finally, Annie can let go to her suppressed grief and weep unashamedly for her one true love.

Marion Fenton lives in Co. Clare. She is married with two grown up children. She retired recently from nursing. She has done a few courses in creative writing and has written a few short, autobiographical fiction stories over the last few years. This is her first entry in a writing competition.

Yellow Blossoms

By Ian Campbell,
Ormeau Road, Belfast

Two elderly brothers, one living in the city and the other still on the family farm, are both feeling the weight of their years and illness and it falls to one of the sons to be their regular visitor. Uncle James had been a forbidding figure on childhood visits to the farm but routine contact now in later life brings about a more tolerant appreciation between them …

WE HAD HOPED, my mother and me, that my father would be released from hospital before Easter. Under pressure, the consultant agreed to let him home for two days in the Easter holidays, but said he wanted him back as soon as possible as my father was an ill man and the stroke was only part of it.

About two days before he was due to come home I sat dozing in the heat and quiet of his room. He reached and took my wrist in a vice-like grip.

'You won't forget about James?'

'I think I have enough to do coming down here without going up there as well.'

His grip tightened, forcing me to look him in the eyes. 'He'll need your help, it's not just me who's ill and let's face it I will not be back at the farm anyway soon. He's the only one left now. I know he's not an easy man, but he has a good heart and I know he will appreciate it … even if he can't show it.'

He held onto my wrist until I mumbled some sort of agreement. He put his head back on the pillow, his eyes closed, content in the knowledge he had gotten his own way again. I leaned back in my chair, my eyelids growing heavy again and my thoughts drifting to my uncle, Samuel James.

James was the middle brother of my father's family at 78. My father was the youngest at 68. There were six others, all male. All became tradesmen and left the farm once they were all time-served joiners and scattered like hand-sewn seed to Canada, USA and South Africa. Photos and letters were sent home in the early days, but faded with the passage of time. They never returned to the farm. James and my father stayed and worked the land until my father met my mother and they moved to Belfast.

As a child I remember going to the farm when my father went to visit. On reaching Baillies Mills, our little baby Austin bounced over the stones in the long loanin, while on the back seat sat a wicker basket half-full of food, home-made soda bread, a freshly cooked ham, a family packet of loose tea and his favourite 'potato apple' baked by my grandmother who was a country woman from Kells.

The end of the lane opened into a yard wide enough to turn a tractor. The house stood on the left, the outhouses forming a square and everything surrounded by fields.

There was always smoke from the chimney, winter and summer, grey and wispy in the summer months, dark and full of sparks, with the sound of crackling timber in winter time.

The two would greet each other with a nod. I was ignored. They would sit by the range and talk in low tones, with the occasional hiss as James spat into the fire, a trait I hated. I would leave the house at this point for some air.

I would explore the outhouses, now disused and creepy, the old tack room with worn harness and horse collars, all mounted half-way up the wall on rusty chains that would clink as the evening breeze moved them. Thick cobwebs clung to the old wooden stalls and brickwork. I would wonder what size of spider lived in here. I would test myself to see how far I could walk into the deepening darkness.

But there was always something real or imagined at the periphery of my vision, a shape skulking into a corner, a feeling of being watched from above by something clinging to the rafters, its sinewy body pressed against the corrugated tin of the roof. It was then my courage would fail me and I would run back to the light and safety of the house.

At the end of our visit, James stood framed by the half door and raised an arm as the car pulled away. I felt the salute was aimed at my father only. He never noticed me and didn't seem to care the feeling was mutual.

A week had now passed and still I hadn't been to see James. So to stop my father getting agitated, that weekend I put some food in the car and headed for Baillies Mills. It had been a long time since I'd been to the farm. The long loanin had gone from bumpy to pot-holed, except for the rise in the middle which was high with tall grasses and green mould which clung limpet-like to the loose stones. The briars and hedges, no longer cut back, reached like thorny fingers for the body of the car, then suddenly I was in the farm yard.

The house was smaller than I had remembered it. It hadn't been whitewashed for some time. A melancholy air of neglect hung over the buildings. A few wisps of weak smoke trailed over the Bangor Blue slates. I lifted the latch and pushed open the door.

James sat hunched over a low fire in a woollen cardigan, a muffler around his neck.

'It's me, Robert, John's son.'

51

He half turned and made some kind of greeting but I couldn't make it out. The creel by the range was empty.

'Have you any logs round the back?'

He nodded.

I went outside and split enough logs to fill the creel. I could feel my forehead damp with exertion. Soon the sparks were flying up the wide chimney and the warmth was creeping over the quarry tiles to our feet. I made him a mug of strong tea and a soda bread slice thick with butter. But I noticed he had difficulty swallowing.

'Is the throat giving you trouble?' He waved a hand to dismiss the question.

'Have you any help? Does anyone come in?'

He reached to the fireplace and gave me a piece of wrinkled paper, on it the name and phone number of the family two fields away. I heard him croak, 'A good woman.' I copied the number down. We talked for a while about my father, but I could see it was difficult for him. I asked him if there was anything I could do before I left. He said something that sounded like 'win'. I asked him again.

'Whinn branches,' he said. 'With the yellow blossoms still on.'

Not wishing to ask any more I went to the back field and got some whinns with the yellow blossom. I split some more logs and brought both whinns and logs and set them in the creel. 'What are they for?' I asked, nodding at the whinns. He just tapped the side of his nose and smiled.

We said our goodbyes and I left. All the way home the image of James stayed in my mind.

Two days later I phoned Mrs. Patterson and explained who I was. She remembered my father. I asked what she thought of James. She told me he had been in ill health for some time. His throat was the main trouble. Some days he could only drink soup. She had tried to get him to see a doctor but he flatly refused. 'He's very thran.'

'It runs in the family,' I told her, 'Stubbornness inbred.' I thanked her and told her to ring me any time she needed to.

I visited James a week later. As well as the food I took him a half-bottle of Black Bush. His eyes brightened as he laced his tea with whiskey. He was in better form. I asked him did he want to visit my father. It was a waste of time but I think he understood I had to ask. The truth was they would never see each other again.

Before I left I split some more logs, cut some whinn branches with blossoms on. I left again without knowing what they were for. My father had gone back into hospital so making regular visits to James was harder now, but I had managed to keep it all going.

The visits to James had routine now, sharing tea, a Black Bush, splitting logs, cutting whinn branches. We had gone from tolerating each other to accepting who we were. He was no longer the ogre of my childhood, I was no longer the smartalec he remembered. Perhaps blood was thicker than water after all and I was turning into my father with every visit.

Phone calls late at night never bring good news. Mrs. Patterson said she had noticed James was having real difficulty eating anything. She sent for the doctor who sent him straight to hospital. I took down the details and thanked her.

On my first visit to the hospital he had been moved to Intensive Care. He was fed through a tube and all his vital signs were being monitored. It was ten days before the inevitable happened. They said he died peacefully in his sleep. I found it hard to believe it was peaceful. There was now a funeral to arrange and to keep all this from my father who was sinking slowly with every visit.

After James's funeral was over I took one last look around the farm. Under the kitchen window there was a mound of dried-out tea leaves and among them the washed-out shrivelled heads of whinn blossoms.

At my last call with Mrs Patterson I gave her a bunch of flowers, we had tea and chatted. I mentioned the tea leaves in the dump with whinn blossoms. She put her hands over her eyes and rocked slightly then lowered her hands, her eyes now moist, 'Poor James.' She explained it was an old country cure, more folklore than anything else. The older generation believed boiling the yellow blossom and drinking the juice would cure a septic throat. 'It wouldn't cure what James had, but he wasn't to know that.'

The telling of all this to my father was taken out of my hands when he died four weeks later. He was buried in the same family plot behind the Covenanters Church.

With everything over, I walked to the entrance gate and passed the fresh grave of James. There on the mound of soil someone had fashioned a spray of whinn bushes, the yellow blossom standing out in the sunlight.

I suppose most people regard whinn bushes as weeds. I see them a lot different now as did my father's generation. They had respect for the yellow blossom.

Ian Campbell is married and has one son. He retired nine years ago. He started writing forty years ago and still belongs to Ards Writers, believed to be the longest existing writing circle in Northern Ireland. Over the years he has had seven or eight stories published in Ireland's Own *magazine. In 2013, he had his book of stories,* Tales From Titanic City, *published.*

Daddy's Hands

By Aidan Grennan,
Killina, Co. Offaly

Daddy had the hands to take on any job, and the brains to see it through, from thinning beet, mending the family shoes and cutting turf to thatching his own and the neighbours' houses, but those hands had a gentle touch of humanity in them too …

DADDY'S HANDS WERE the hands of a gentleman. Daddy's hands earned their bread by hard work and by honest endeavour. If necessity was the mother of invention, then my father was her husband. He belonged to a generation of rural Irish people who never knew the meaning of being spoon-fed, except as infants.

Daddy toiled virtually all his life, on a small, unforgiving Offaly farm. Poverty rode with him for company.

Daddy's hands cut the turf, saved the hay, built walls, sank wells, thinned beet, mended the family footwear and white-washed the family home. In addition, he thatched homes for neighbours as well as his own. Daddy had the hands to take on any job, and the brains to see it through.

Once I watched him manufacture his very own farmyard truck for moving sacks of grain or whatever else needed moving. It was a sturdy piece of work, bearing all the hallmarks of his talent.

Daddy's hands could turn used flower bags into quality sheets, fit to keep an Eskimo warm.

But those same hands had a gentle touch of humanity in them too. They sympathised with many a grief-stricken neighbour on the loss of a loved one, and they wished numerous brides and grooms 'the height of good luck', as they set out on the pot-holed road of married life.

Daddy's hands also steered a non-too-reliable bicycle to the Eucharistic Congress in Dublin. That was on Sunday, 26th of June, 1932 – the day he turned twenty-eight years of age. Three years later, the same hands – and almost certainly the same bicycle – guided their way to Dublin again, this time to see the Limerick v Kilkenny All-Ireland senior hurling final.

And there, beneath a sky of lead, he saw his idol, the great Lory Meagher from Tullaroan, send a rain-sodden sliotar over Limerick's crossbar, from 90 yards. Daddy loved the wristy style used by the Kilkenny hurlers. He had been a fairly decent hurler himself, playing a bit with the famed 'Rahan Reds'.

My father's hands carried the talent of being able to 'divine' for water. Several times I studied him with a 'Y'-shaped hazel rod in his special hands, and I noted how the stick would bend when water was below. Another talent he had was the 'grafting' of apple trees, ensuring new fruit came into existence.

Daddy's hands filled out crossword puzzles, were successful at many a whist drive, held his adored *Irish Press* newspaper and marked the numbers at numerous Bingo sessions. He loved his 'Western' books where his favourite character was 'Sudden' and his favourite author, Zane Grey.

Like countless Irish homes, the Rosary was said nightly. My father came into his own for this solemn ceremony. We had the Joyful, Sorrowful and Glorious Mysteries. The Sorrowful Mysteries were especially touching: The Agony in the Garden, The Scourging at the Pillar, The Crowning with Thorns, The Carrying of the Cross and The Crucifixion. During the five decades, my father fed each bead through his ageing fingers, pondering on the Lord's suffering as he did so.

The Hail Holy Queen and the Litany of the Blessed Virgin Mary followed the Rosary, and these in turn were followed by

The Trimmings, a lengthy selection of powerful prayers which my father rhymed off like the six-times tables in Primary School.

Repairing bicycle punctures was a never-ending mission in my father's life. Often, we'd watch him upend a bicycle on our kitchen floor and set to work. Two dessert spoons or hefty forks were used to remove the tube from inside the tyre, then a yellow Dunlop Cycle Puncture Repair Outfit box was opened and this contained the basics for mending the offending puncture.

A basin of water was used to highlight where the air was escaping from the tube. And then, when the mission was complete, the tube would be pumped up again and soon the waiting cyclist would be ready to continue on their journey.

Daddy lived to the age of 79. For most of his final four years he was confined to bed in Tullamore Hospital, but was allowed home for the occasional weekend if he had the necessary strength. It was in that hospital that he passed away on October 18, 1983. Despite our countless visits to his bedside, he died alone. It was one of those things that was meant to be.

We got the call to rush in but he had passed on minutes before our breathless arrival. The nurses comforted us as we tried to take in the fact that he had gone. Fittingly, they had placed the Cross showing the crucified Christ in Daddy's hands.

Aidan Grennan has had many articles published in Ireland's Own *over the past 22 years. Included in his work were three series,* Remembering the 20th Century, Your Town, *and* Our GAA County Ground Names. *In November 2018 he published his first book,* Memories of Rahan, *a collection of stories from his native parish. He is married to Martina for 37 years and is employed as a Clerical Officer with the Department of Education in Tullamore.*

It's Never Too Late

By Ben O'Dea,
Liscarroll, Mallow, Co. Cork

Paddy opted to leave his little village home in Ireland, and Maura, and head to London where he worked on the buildings. As with so many before, the weeks and months drifted into years and decades and he took solace in the pub and in drink. However, his memories of home were never quite erased and he clung to the hope of returning …

THE ROAD LOOKED just the same to Paddy, as he walked slowly towards the little house of his birth; maybe a few new houses here and there but still the road remained as Paddy remembered it so many years ago. As he came to the bridge that spanned the lazily flowing little stream, he rested his elbows on the time worn parapet and gazed nostalgically upstream towards the towering mountains as Maura and himself oft times did so long, long ago.

How many years now since he'd kissed her and said his goodbye at this very spot? It seemed like only yesterday, yet almost thirty years had passed since that tearful farewell. 'I've nothing to keep me here now,' he'd said to Maura after his mother was laid to rest in the old church yard beside his father. He never remembered his father as he had died when he was only one year old. His mother had doted on him for the next twenty years before losing the unequal struggle against cancer.

'Tomorrow,' said Paddy 'I'll be off to England. Sure I can lock up the little house and 'twill be waiting there if I ever think of coming back.'

'I'll be waiting too Paddy,' whispered Maura, a look of pain in her beautiful blue eyes.

The first little twinges of doubt crept over Paddy as the boat sailed away from Rosslare harbour. Maura's blue eyes seemed to be gazing across the water as his beloved homeland slipped below the horizon.

The smoke and grime of London was a far cry from the clear, healthy air and green fields of home and Paddy vowed that his stay would be short in this monstrous concrete jungle. The days passed into weeks, then months, then years as he toiled on the building sites until home was almost forgotten. Yet, whenever someone would sing that Percy French classic, *Come Back Paddy Reilly*, it seemed especially meant for him, and Maura's eyes would seem to gaze longingly into his own.

Maura and himself had exchanged letters for the first year or so but as Paddy moved about from place to place on his job and kept changing his address, the letters became fewer until finally Paddy stopped writing altogether. Each night Paddy would pass away the time in some public house. The 'craic' was good and soon the drink became an all-consuming habit and not one night would pass but he would have his quota of beer or whiskey.

At times he would think of Maura and home; it was then the grief and sorrow of his wasted life would hit him hard and he would indulge in a bout of drinking which would leave him senseless and deaden his mind to his sorrows.

Thus the years turned into decades. As he grew older, Paddy became obsessed with the idea of someday returning home and being reunited there with his beloved Maura. It was this obsession which really kept him going throughout the hard working days and long lonesome nights.

At last the hard work and even harder living had caught up with Paddy. Consumption, or as it was now known tuberculosis, had riddled his abused lungs. He'd spent a long term in hospital and even though he'd had the very best of treatment, nothing could be done to repair his diseased body. Discharging himself from the hospital, Paddy decided to spend the little time he'd left amongst all the friends of his long lost youth.

Would he see Maura again? If so, he would die a happy man. Packing his few belongings into an old suitcase, he had bought a one-way ticket to Rosslare via Paddington and Fishguard. As he boarded the train at Paddington station, he took one last look at the city which had destroyed him, or maybe he had destroyed himself!

He scarcely remembered the long journey to Fishguard or the crossing to Rosslare harbour. A tiredness seemed to have entered every fibre of his being. He boarded a bus that would take him to the bottom of the road which winded its way uphill to the village which had always held a very special place in his heart. Eventually, he alighted at the place he remembered so well and almost dragged his tired old body towards the bridge which held such bitter-sweet memories.

His day dreaming ended. Paddy walked slowly up the hill to the spot where his little home once stood. But all that was left were four crumbling, ivy covered walls and where daffodils, tulips and wall flowers once grew in abundance, weeds and nettles now formed an impregnable barrier.

Next he came to the crossroads where Maura and himself used to gather with all the local boys and girls to dance the beautiful summer evenings away on the little wooden platform, or 'stage' as it was better known, to the music of the fiddle and melodeon, played with great gusto by old Jim McCann and Billy Callaghan, whilst Jerry Moloney kept time on the drums as well as acting M.C. and rendering some of the long forgotten ballads in a rich tenor voice.

Nobody seemed to have a care in the world with faces glowing from the exertions of dancing and sheer happiness. Maura and himself would stroll home hand in hand, dreaming their dreams as young lovers the world over do. Jim, Billy and Jerry would have passed to their eternal reward long ago. What of the others? Emigration would have taken its toll but some had probably settled down to married life and raised families. Maybe Maura had 'settled down'.

Paddy's suitcase seemed a lot heavier now as he trudged wearily uphill towards the little village of his birth. He finally came to a smart new bungalow with a B&B sign on the window. A pleasant young woman answered his timid knock on the door and he booked in for the night. As he rested his tired body in a comfortable chair in his spotless room, he thought back on his wasted life.

Suddenly he stood erect on his aching feet and said to nobody in particular, 'Paddy McAuliffe, you're a coward. You were a coward when you ran away from reality all those years ago, you were a coward when you passed Maura's house just a while ago, but by God you'll put your cowardliness to one side and you'll go down now to Maura's house.'

So saying, he marched down the road to Maura's house with a new spring in his step. The children had disappeared from the garden and as he walked up the footpath and knocked on the door, he wondered if Maura was at home or even if she was still alive?

As the door was opened, Paddy caught his breath at the sight of a beautiful, matured woman. Her fair hair was just a little tinged with grey and her face seemed a little older but it was Maura alright, with a quizzical look in her eyes. 'Can I help you?' she asked politely.

'You wouldn't recognise me Maura after all the years but I'm your old friend from the past, Paddy McAuliffe.' A look of disbelief came over Maura's face, 'Come in Paddy' she said in a shocked voice. 'You're the last person in the world I expected to see.' Maura led the way into a beautiful sitting room. 'You look terrible Paddy,' she said. 'Sit down there and I'll plug in the kettle.'

Paddy sat down on a nice soft bottomed chair and drew in a lungful of clear Irish air. 'What a fool I was to leave such a beautiful, healthy country and venture to that God forsaken unhealthy environment,' he thought, as Maura wheeled in a small table with a tray full of lovely buttered scones, a steaming pot of tea, milk, sugar and two large mugs.

'Dainty little cups are only for ladies,' smiled Maura. 'Now tell me what brings you back after all the years?' Maura stared into Paddy's face and suddenly she could see the pain and sadness in his eyes. 'You're not well Paddy,' she almost whispered.

'I'm not Maura,' Paddy replied. 'I've got tuberculosis, I was told in the hospital that it was incurable but the local G.P. told me I had a chance if I had certain food and plenty of fresh air.'

'You'll certainly have good food and plenty of fresh air here Paddy. My daughter is just parking her car outside as she collects her children at this time every evening. The three of us will sit down and come up with some idea, we've certainly a lot of things to talk about.'

Just then, the front door opened and a beautiful young woman stepped inside. 'Patricia, I think you had better sit down on the sofa, you may be in for a big shock!' Patricia sat down and looking around her said, 'Am I missing something here?'

'You've been missing something for almost twenty-seven years. Patricia, may I introduce you to somebody very special. Say hello to your father, Patrick McAuliffe!' There was a stunned silence in the room, then suddenly Paddy and Patricia jumped up and rushed into each other's arms. Maura joined them and the tears started to flow.

'Why didn't you tell me Maura?' said a tearful Paddy.

'I was too proud,' said Maura 'and as time went on I didn't want to upset my lovely little daughter but now it's a terrible load off my mind.'

Paddy looked at Maura and wondered at her marvellous will power and love. Holding Maura's two hands in his own, he looked into her eyes and said 'Maura, is it too late to ask you to marry me?'

'It's never too late Paddy,' whispered Maura, hugging him tightly. Suddenly two little fireballs leapt into Paddy's arms screaming 'We've a new Grandad, we've a new Grandad.'

Yes, thought Paddy, you have a Grandad alright, but not a very new one.

Paddy was a new man, 'Maura' he said 'For every week during all those years, I put away some money in the bank. I haven't touched that so there's a good few quid in there. Also my cards were 'stamped' all those years plus I got a nice lump sum in redundancy. I'll do up the old house, I know it will cost a lot but I'll spare nothing on it and when it's finished I'll give it as a present to my lovely daughter and her family. It's the least I can do after all those missing years. So here's to the future, I know I'll be ok now.'

At last Paddy knew that coming home was the right decision.

Ben O'Dea was born in 1934 in a little village in North Cork. He can vividly remember the hardships and great fear during the war years, but the family were never hungry or cold. During his school days, writing was his favourite subject. As he grew older he began to write stories, poems and songs for his own enjoyment. He worked driving heavy machinery and writing was a form of relaxation. Now retired, he still enjoys writing and can spend more time with his lifelong friend and wife, Kathleen, and their six children, grandchildren and great grandchildren.

A Grief that Convulsed the Nation

By Joe Connolly,
Newbridge, Co. Kildare

Having been chosen to serve in the Irish army in 1960, it was very early in his military training that word filtered through that tragedy had fallen the first group of Irish personnel to serve overseas with the United Nations in The Congo and that nine men were killed by local tribesmen. One of his first duties was to serve in the guard of honour when they were laid to rest after a massive funeral turn-out in Dublin …

FOLLOWING A HAPPY school life, the time had finally arrived to select a career. It was 1960; there were only a small number of job opportunities to choose from. I applied for an apprenticeship with the Army Signal Corps and to the delight of my family, I was selected. I enlisted in mid-October with very little idea of what lay ahead.

Over the years, old comrades gathered to recall memories of those first six months of initial military training. I also recall the camaraderie of training with new friends, wearing a uniform made of what was then called 'Bull's Wool', rising for Reveille at 7.00 am, standing in formation, long route marches, endless hours of running, jumping, crawling through dirt, foot drill called 'square bashing', and arms poked full of needles with every imaginable kind of vaccination.

Army instructors who dealt with recruits screamed orders and pushed them to their physical limit. Our idols were Elvis and later The Beatles and we all arrived with the 'quiff' and sidelocks kept in place with Brylcreem. The Army barber left us all devastated.

1960 also marked a very exciting year in the history of the Irish army, with two battalions stationed overseas for the first time. In June, Ireland had answered the United Nations call for a peacekeeping mission to the newly independent Congo.

We had been less than four weeks into our training when we woke to rumours of an encounter with those troops stationed in far off Africa. In those pre-Internet and 'rolling news' days, communication was slow and sometimes uncertain. The nation was stunned when An Taoiseach, Mr. Seán Lemass, made the announcement on Radio Éireann that on the 8th November eleven Irish troops were missing with fears for their safety. The nation held its breath before it was finally confirmed that nine were dead.

With immediate effect the army authorities formed a plan for their homecoming and burial, and orders were given that all serving personnel were to take part. Our foot drill and weapons training became very intense on the days leading up to the funeral with up to eight hours each day on the barrack square.

The story of that 33rd Battalion began in August 1960 and half way through their six-month stint, on that fateful 8th November day, a patrol made up of members of this battalion had approached the village of Niemba with orders to repair a bridge outside the town.

The platoon was forced to leave their vehicles and was soon surrounded by over one hundred Baluba tribesmen armed with spears, bows and clubs. They came under attack and the officer in command, Lieut Kevin Gleeson, was beaten to death while covering the retreat of his men. Their vehicles held Lee Enfield rifles, Gustav submachine guns and Bren light machine guns but they were cut off from their weapons and killed in hand-to-hand fighting.

The story for eight of the men – Gleeson, Gaynor, Dougan, Kelly, Killeen, Farrell, McGuinn and Fennell – ended when the plane carrying their bodies landed as fog hung over Baldonnel airdrome, from where a few months earlier they had been lifted in a giant transport plane into a summer sky looking forward to the adventure of a lifetime. The ninth body, that of Trooper Browne, was recovered two years later.

After a short service on the 22nd November, attended by President de Valera and Chief of Staff, Major General Seán MacEoin, the cortège moved like massive plinths bearing the flag-draped coffins, followed by the band of the Curragh Training Camp. As bells tolled from churches throughout the city, green clad soldiers in slow marching steps were gripped in pride and grief during that ten-mile trip from Baldonnel to Glasnevin Cemetry.

Thousands lined the streets and men, women and children knelt in prayer and many wept openly. Bigger and bigger the crowd grew, filling the main streets and overflowing into side streets. Four army jeeps followed, crammed with wreaths and Mass cards.

I stood for over three hours on the Finglas road close to the gates of Glasnevin Cemetery in full military uniform armed with a Lee Enfield rifle, as I awaited an instruction from my commanding officer. Silently, the cortege rolled up the Finglas Road where I, with two hundred other Irish Troops, reversed arms in eerie silence, bowed our heads as the gun carriage and four army trucks passed by and entered the gates of Glasnevin Cemetery.

In those hallowed surroundings, I heard the firing party's salute marking the end of a long journey. Eight brave Irish soldiers were finally laid to rest in a common military grave close to the resting place of Michael Collins, in the shadow of the lofty O'Connell Monument.

With less than six weeks service I had participated in my first Guard of Honour on a day when there occurred perhaps the biggest outpouring of grief Ireland has seen in modern times, a day engraved in my memory forever.

Joe Connolly has been prominent on the Irish amateur drama scene. He was a member of the Rathangan Players when they won the All-Ireland title in Athlone with a production of Da. *He won the 'Best Lighting' award at the Waterford International Festival of Light Opera with Kill Musical Society in a production of* Fiddler on the Roof *and he was Highly Commended in the 2018* Ireland's Own' Anthology. *He has self-published three books on the history of the local musical and drama scene, under the general title* From Behind the Spotlight. *He has a number of memoirs published on the Writing.ie website.*

Short Story

The House of the Spirit

By Kathleen O'Brien,
Ballyporeen, Co. Tipperary

'I want to go home to die,' she had said. The doctor and the home care nurses had been persuaded that she'd be no bother, that everything would flow and fall into place. After all, we knew her as an independent woman, more than capable of taking care of herself. To be fair, it never occurred to any of us that dying could take so long ...

IF MEMORY SERVES me right it was during the last days of October, as she was heading into winter, the time they took her leg off. It had rained all week and windfalls were rotting in the orchard grass. Nobody was saying much, since any word was the wrong thing to say with her sharp tongue, and the heart gone out of her. She was ready, she said, to say goodbye, as she clutched a cross in her withered hand.

And yet she had never seemed so lost. She was trying to believe in a god that she hadn't given a second thought to in her happy days, but had suddenly become someone that she would face before long.

Outside her window the rain clouds passed, and as she lay on her iron bed with her limbs relaxed the watery sun was shining in bars of light across her face. When she asked me to look at her stump, like it was a badge of courage, she looked softer, almost at peace, with clouds in her eyes.

If she had passed then, what a load of trouble she would have saved herself and everyone who came to care for her.

She sat in the only chair in the small room at the nursing home, under a window which was never opened, at the mercy of the weather that glared down on her pink scalp and her shabby brown dress. 'I'm tired of people coming in and out,' she whispered. 'I'm tired of faces I don't know.'

The state she was in then! Shapeless! Huddled against the arm of the chair, her one leg was a plank that kept her body upright. 'My suitcase is in the bottom of the wardrobe,' she said. 'I could be out of here in ten minutes.' The grief in the twisted hands would draw tears from a stone.

It helped that the doctor was on his high horse the day I went to his surgery. 'I agree with her! She'll be gaga after six months. Half of them shouldn't be there in the first place.'

He signed the release form with a flourish. The details are a muddle in my head now, but I see her sharp face all smiles, the inmates crying as she waves them goodbye from her new wheel-chair, the matron tight-lipped as a cash-paying guest departs.

So she came back from the nursing home. A good deed you might say, for a friend of my late mother, and the sun shone down on us as we drove away. 'Did you empty the wardrobe?' she said. 'Are you sure that you left nothing behind?'

Her next door neighbour, Mary, was waiting at her little house and it's fair to say that we basked in the general feeling that comes with an act of kindness. Why wouldn't you be kind to someone who had no living relative? Although I must confess that her tears wore me down, even knowing from experience that tears could be faked.

I had done nothing except bring her home in her hour of need. Looking back, it makes me wonder how little we all knew, believing that she would settle in as before. It seemed that autumn day would last forever, since both the doctor and my mean soul told me that she could be dead by Christmas.

On the day she arrived home her old friend, Jo, had lit the cranky stove and the kitchen was warm. Mary had cleaned the window and she could see her patchwork fields as they ran down to the village as far as the church steeple. It seemed a good omen. Yet she was no sooner inside the door than she started to complain. Even the cat looked lost, she said. It didn't look like his home anymore either.

'Where's the sofa?' she said, and I answered that the sofa had gone to make space for the wheelchair. She moved quickly around the table in the wheelchair as if it was a racing car.

'No! No! No! Use your head! Bring it back right now! What will my visitors sit on? Do you expect me to live in a house that's upside down?'

I dropped her bundle of clothes, glorified rags really, by the bedroom door and told her that I'd had enough. She stared at me, her thoughts working overtime. 'So you don't want to come any more,' she said, 'that's alright, that's okay. At least stay, stay and have a cup of tea.' I was already on the way out. I even had the car keys in my hand. I should have left then and never come back.

I relive that moment over and over again in a dream where I hear the closing of a door.

'I want to go home to die,' she had said. The doctor and the home care nurses had been persuaded that she'd be no bother, that everything would flow and fall into place. After all, we knew her as an independent woman, more than capable of taking care of herself.

To be fair, it never occurred to any of us that dying could take so long, the years of visits to the hospital in the small hours, sitting beside her as she tried to persuade a young doctor with dark shadows under his eyes that it could be his mother lying on a trolley waiting for a bed. Later, she turned to me.

'What would you do with yourself if you weren't here? You might as well be here as anywhere else.'

Wrong again.

Once, I invented a holiday in London in order to cut off all contact and let her see that I was not dependent on her, that it was, in fact, the other way around. I returned a week later carrying a potted red geranium and a postcard of Buckingham Palace that said 'Wish you were here!'

She looked at the card without comment. Then she sniffed the plant. 'Put it over there on the window sill,' she said. 'There's no place else to put it. Or you could always take it away again. There's a whiff from it like a dead body.'

After a while, I began to see that happiness can be found in unexpected places. This was how she would live her life. I've never sat down to try and figure out what drew me back. I made excuses to myself. What if she died in the night? Would I be able to live with the guilt, if guilt was the correct word? Would it bring me luck to extend the hand of friendship to an old woman? These were the thoughts that came to me.

When I did go back after a few days absence, and let myself into the dim kitchen with my own key where she was napping by the stove, her face lit up. Tears came to her eyes and there was a hint of something in my own. The weight of her friendship and the rare words of gratitude were like a beam of sunshine in the gloom.

As time passed on, the thought uppermost in my mind was that if you start something you must finish it. This could mean stirring an evil smelling chicken hot pot on the stove, or throwing in a potato or a carrot so that it lasted her for two or three days. What I did begin to understand was how firm a grip she had in the here and now, the belief she had that she could cope with anything once she was home.

Her favourite topic of conversation was her pain. In the draughty kitchen, without hope or without despair, discussions took place on the broken skin of a heel, the shoe that leaned on the on/off bunion, how to treat an ingrown toenail. Sometimes there were stomach pains, and there was always the shoulder pain that she blamed on being manhandled into bed.

She treated the arrival of each pain like an unwanted visitor, with surprise and shock. There was a handkerchief pinned to her cardigan for such emergencies. It could not possibly be happening to her, not when she was living her re-imagined life as a young girl. Sometimes if she was feeling under the weather, as she put it, there was a sense of relief in letting go and sniffling along with her.

There is something more you should know. Her problem with a god who doesn't listen can be traced back to an experience in the early years after she got married, and the night she woke up and found warm, sticky blood on the worn sheet. Her husband, Tom, got the bike from the shed and she sat on the crossbar. She lost the baby in the dark and the pouring rain between the potholed road and the doctor's house a few miles away. She had come late to marriage, she said, but she'd die happy if she was convinced that she'd meet her child again.

She would never again walk. That's a thought that's unknowable to us even in our dreams. What was remarkable was how quickly she learned to adapt to her new reality, after the prayers and the pleas and the bargaining with her god had fallen on deaf ears.

'The leg will have to be buried,' she said. 'And it must be put down in the grave with Tom's remains when no one is looking.' In a strange way, she understood that she was sending the leg back to where it came from. She looked at me with her watery eyes. 'What they won't know won't trouble them. I'm depending on you.'

She had a dread of poverty that could only have come from what she called 'the good old days.' She reached out to callers with bread and ham from the local shop. 'Stay! What hurry is on you? You're only in the door. Or am I confusing the time? The clock says a quarter to five. Make tea! Make tea! Why doesn't anyone want to drink tea anymore?'

On the days that she stayed in bed, having trouble with the waterworks, a visitor would perch on the edge of the wheelchair in front of a bundle of adult nappies, while she laughed over a dance in the village hall half a century before. Her clothes from the previous night waited in a little heap on the floor beside the bed, a lavender blouse, an old slip, a moth-eaten cardigan that cost a lot of money a lot of years ago.

It would be too sentimental and easy to say that I had feelings of affection for her, because these feelings were often mingled with ill-temper and low spirits on a day of damp wood in a smoky kitchen. But on that same evening, a curious sun peeped in the window. 'Sunny side up!' she screamed, and we laughed till our sides were sore. When I walked out into the yard, the sky looked brighter, almost luminous.

How do I explain her leaving? Her moth breath is on the pillow, with the window slightly open to let the spirit out. The birds are waiting on the wire. The fields elbow their way down the valley but up here we are touching the sky. The light hovers on a cloud of white hair.

We become our choices. I wonder if she has brought out the best in me. Soon enough she'll be gone, far away from here. Meanwhile, we share this air together. I am surprised that it matters and how much it matters.

Kathleen O'Brien took early retirement from teaching English, and got bored with not having any creative outlet. Encouraged by her son to join a writing class, she applied for, and got accepted on the Masters in Creative Writing Course at University College, Cork. While she did her thesis in poetry, she has recently started to write short stories in a dusty, soon-to-be demolished attic.

The Green Beetle

By Eileen Caplice,
Dromore, Mallow, Co. Cork

Are you coming for a spin?' they asked casually. I couldn't believe it. They were taking the car that our mother was about to buy. She might just as easily change her mind! 'Come on we'll be quick, get in' they said. But I was chicken and screamed after them 'I'll tell, I'll tell.'

THERE WERE TWO black Beetles in our parish. Fr. Kennefick, the curate, drove one and Nora O'Leary, the district nurse and midwife, drove the other. Cars were scarce on country roads in the '60s and almost all Beetles were black. But when I got home from school, there was a green Beetle parked outside the gate and I wondered who our visitor might be.

Going in the pathway, my mother and Danny Cusack were coming out against me. 'Your dinner is in the Aga,' she said to me. 'I'm taking the car for a drive with Danny.' He was the village car dealer so it struck me that he was trying to make a sale.

Upon returning, I overheard her say, 'I'll take it.' Hopping with excitement, dinner was abandoned and I raced back to the front gate to get a better look at the Beetle. It had an oval rear windscreen. It was a 1950s model, successor to the earlier version with the split back window and outstretched arm indicators that returned to flush when not in use. A car of our own! Could it be true?

When I got there, my brother, Tom, and sister, Mary, were ensconced in the front seats with Tom sitting brazenly behind the wheel. 'Are you coming for a spin?' they asked casually as Tom turned the key that was left dangling in the ignition. I couldn't believe it.

They were taking the car that our mother was about to buy. She might just as easily change her mind! 'Come on we'll be quick, get in' they said. But I was chicken and screamed after them 'I'll tell, I'll tell.'

'We'll kill you if you do,' they yelled out the windows as they pulled away.

When I saw the back of the Beetle disappearing around Beecher's Bend, I panicked. Turning and racing down the path, through the front door, across the hall and into the kitchen, I shouted 'They're gone, they're gone.'

'Who's gone?' my mother asked. 'Tom and Mary, they're gone with the car,' I roared. My mother had cheque-book open and pen in hand. Both she and Danny leapt from their chairs and followed me at breakneck speed back up the path and out onto the road. Lo and behold, there was the car, gone.

My mother in a fury demanded to know 'Which way? Which way?' Danny nearly had a fit when I pointed towards Beecher's Bend. We took off running over the road with Danny on his bad bandy legs trailing behind us. Around the farm the story gathered momentum and Bob, Eddie, Willie, Margaret and Jeanie joined the hunt for the fugitives as the word was out that 'the sky was falling down'. With no sign of the rally-drivers, we were beginning to think they had crashed.

Farmers' children of those times would have been driving tractors from aged nine or ten so. At twelve, Tom was cocky and full of bravado. He and Mary were 'Irish twins' born in the same year, thick as thieves and up to every devilment.

However, when they got as far as Jim Beecher's and felt maybe they had gone too far, Tom found the car wasn't for turning.

Mary got out and cheekily knocked on Jim's door and asked him to come and help them find reverse. Without question, Jim turned the Beetle so the joy-riders could continue on their grand tour. It didn't bother him that they were only twelve years old and never even asked where they got the car.

Meanwhile, the search party was well down the road when the distinctive sound of the Volkswagen was heard and the two appeared on their return trip. With just the tops of their heads showing above the dash, KI 7405 came into view. My mother frantically waved them down, commanding them to stop. 'Get out of that car ye pair of brats,' she shouted.

Tom brought the car to a sudden halt in the middle of the road. Flinging open the doors, both jumped out and ran for their lives, Tom scaling the ditch on the driver's side and Mary clambering over a dry stone wall on the other. My mother calling after them 'Yer father will kill ye' only made them run faster. The rule was, if devilment was being done, everyone was to scatter so that nobody got caught.

Out of his mind and worked up to a froth, Danny ran around the car in circles checking for bangs or scrapes. We all giggled at his antics. Our mother hadn't got as far as paying so his heart was in his mouth.

Anyway, in the end, Danny got his cheque and mother got her Beetle. But after that she kept the keys on a chain around her neck.

Eileen Caplice only took up writing in recent years while recovering from a series of sporting injuries. She missed out on an Irish cap in veterans tennis after one such injury but she is glad now that her daughter, Anna, has made up for this, somewhat, with several international caps in Womens' Rugby to date. She believes it is important to document all the happenings and stories attaching a fairly typical, large family of the 1950s/60s era because many will probably not be repeated. They will be there to be enjoyed, hopefully, by readers, including her children and grandchildren.

To Never Know

By Katherine Carroll,
Church Road, Celbridge, Co. Kildare

*Eileen has a secret from her past and the old tree in the garden
represented almost her only link with that time. While she is away
on her first solo holiday, the family have combined to refurbish
the garden as a surprise for her and she is shocked that the
tree has become a victim of the work ...*

TURNING THE KEY with expectancy, disappointment
hits like a brick when met by silent darkness. 'I can't
believe it, my first solo holiday and no one even missed
me.' Out the kitchen window a small light flickers. I pull across
the sliding doors to investigate. Screams of 'surprise' ring through
the air as confetti from a giant popper cascades over my head.
The excited faces of family illuminate the dusk.

'Do you like your new garden Mam?'

My eyes dart back and forth.

'Mam, don't be so soppy, hope they're tears of joy?'

Terry gives my shoulder a squeeze.

'Sorry it took fifteen years to finish love.'

Everything is swirling, my body is swaying. I wake up, and
rub my temple to appease the pounding. My hand hits a lump
that would make any rugby player's look tame.

Seventeen years old. Little taps on my bedroom
window. I pull across the curtains, squash my
face against the pane, my two best friends stand

giggling by the gate, fistfuls of pebbles ready
to hurl.

'Coming out Eileen?,' they yell up.

'Not tonight.'

'You're turning into an awful bore. How will
you ever find a nice fella to bring to the debs
stuck in that bedroom?'

'Geeky George will have to be your knight in
shining armour,' Elaine roars as they both
erupt into howls of laughter.

'Gotta go, I'm being called.'

'Well we're not letting you off next time.'

I reach under the duvet, pulling out the
chunky knitting needles and soft lemon wool.
Exasperated, I manage only a couple of rows,
my thick, clumsy fingers make every stitch
mastered a trophy.

Pain rips through my body as beads of sweat
line my forehead. Breathing heavily, I shuffle
to my younger sister's bed and shake her. Her
eyes flicker open, then slam shut. The next shake
is more forceful as she groans and pushes my
hand away.

'Bernadette get up, I need your help.'

'Eileen it's the middle of the night, surely it can
wait until morning?'

'I have a pain' I mumble trying to keep the
terror from my voice.

'I'll get Mammy.'

'Don't you dare,' my hysterical tone halting
her in her tracks. 'Do you want to make her sick
again, just help me to the hospital?'

I grab my school bag and wildly start filling it with random things. When Bernadette's back is turned, I throw in my childhood teddy. We make a sorry sight, her stick legs protruding out under the nightdress, almost completely concealed by a chunky hand knitted jumper. The short journey becomes a marathon feat, forced to stop every time the pain becomes unbearable. We reach the granite steps; I give her a quick squeeze, longing to bring her with me, through chattering lips I whisper.

'Off home with you and not a word to anyone in case Mammy gets wind of it. In the morning tell her I'd to go early to school to finish a project and if I'm not back later tell her I am staying over at Sally Anne's.'

'The new girl?'

'Yes, that's the one, now quick before you catch a cold.'

'But you hardly know her.'

'Whist up.'

'Eileen, I'll swap you my slippers for your sneakers' as she pushes them in my direction.

My legs shake so much, I wonder will they carry me to the door. I watch till Bernadette is a speck in the distance. Before I can descend the hospital steps, the large timber door creaks open behind me, as a gruff voice asks me to step inside.

It was two days before the dizziness had subsided and I make it downstairs. Tentatively I pull across the kitchen curtain and peek out, Terry sidling up beside me.

'Like it?'

'Why did you knock my tree?'

'The landscaper said he'd never seen such a strange place to plant a tree, called it overbearing, being nearly in the kitchen.'

'I liked it.'

'Why do you have to be so negative, that garden cost a small fortune, you haven't even said thanks?'

'Sorry, it must be the bump.'

His little finger encircles my fatter one while the nurse in the overly starched uniform bustles around. Not one smile does she throw in our direction.

'You mind that baby well, be sure and bond. The pain of handing him over will stop you repeating the same sin again'? Hard to fathom how she could refer to this beautiful piece of innocence and sin in the same breath.

'Who says I am giving him away?' I scream inwardly.

'Stop snivelling, you are messing up those sheets.'

Hour after hour I stay awake, stubbornly refusing sleep. Every second together is precious. A plan hatches like a beautiful chick. I know the time the nurses take lunch, I whip him from his little cot, clasp him tightly to my chest and throw my coat around us both. I can't manage the school bag. I'll have to devise a plan to tell Mammy. She'll be mad. I make it out unnoticed and head straight for the river path, my heart thumping with excitement. I peek inside my trench coat at the sleeping bundle.

'We are free son, no one barking orders or looking at us with disdain in their eyes.'

Two hours later I shiver uncontrollably as I climb the steps, praying my absence has gone unnoticed. Matron spots me, grabs my arm and frog marches me back to the ward. His little face is scrunched and red with roaring as he's been doing uncontrollably.

'I was just about to call the guards.' For what I wondered, as far as I knew it wasn't a crime to take what belonged to you.

'Do you want to have murder on your conscience too, taking him out in that perishing wind?'

A young nurse comes into the room, not much older than myself.

'Take that dirty baby grow off him, you don't want people to think he is unloved. Hurry along, they're coming.'

I knew to whom she referred, it had been explained or rather told to me. I root in my school bag and pull out the little yellow cardigan. It doesn't quite look like the ones we started life in, courtesy of gran, with the unexplained holes. When the nurse's back is turned I rub him up and down the front of my shirt, determined to keep some part of him. I put my quivering lips against his ear, 'I will come back for you, don't worry, just need to figure it out.' A lone tear mixes with his.

From the pocket of my coat I pull a camera and take a quick snap just as the door opens. Two social workers bustle into the room, without even a hello. They take him from my arms, I take

one last look. They leave, my screams following
the clipping of their heels down the tiled corridor.

Shortly afterwards I am leaving, back down the
cold granite steps. Hysterically, I pull my precious
bear from the bin on the pavement, that I have
spotted it sticking out of. My belly aches as I drag
myself through the open sitting room window
so as not to arouse Mammy's curiosity as to the
whereabouts of my uniform and the blood
stained Snoopy slippers on my feet.

Two days later I'm back, sitting on the rock-
hard school chair. Thankfully, I've a nine-month
stash of sanitary towels. Terrified to ask anyone
about the bleeding. I ache all over. Duran Duran,
are number one and going to be on *Top of the
Pops*. We're all meeting in Roslyn's house to watch
it. I lie awake long into the night, clutching the
check shirt to my sore swollen breasts trying
to figure out how to get the film developed. I fall
asleep in Irish class and get 50 lines, 'the God
fearing go to bed early,' I was told.

Terry insists, someone is with me all the time until I have fully
recovered. I crave solitude. I don't have to set the alarm to wake
at 2am, I slip silently out the back door. I'd given one of my
sleeping tablets to the dog with his dinner. I start to dig. The
half-frozen soil is rock solid. I become frantic. It's pointless.
The dusty pink nail polish my daughter had put on my nails
hours earlier decorates the soil.

At breakfast I broach the subject again of the garden.

'Where's the old tree gone?'

'Mam, are you still harping on about that tree. It was so ugly,
I always hated it,' Donnacha announced.

I felt like he had kicked me, hard, in the stomach.

'We could use it for logs.'

'I think you're forgetting dear that we got a gas fire three years ago.'

'I meant Christmas logs Terry, to remember the tree by.'

'Mam, you're still affected by that knock, who in their right mind remembers a tree?' The kitchen erupts in laughter.

'The gardener had a special machine and he mulched it, took it with him to use on the flowerbeds on the next job.' Mulched! I feel physically sick.

When I had bought the tree, I made sure it was his age. The man in the garden centre told me it was a strange request. Started to delve, but I put a swift stop to his excavation for information. I'd sit under the tree, no matter the season, close my eyes and he was beside me, then climbing above me shaking the branches. His voice filled my ears and joy my heart, until my eyes reopened.

Now with the tree desecrated and the tin box with my only photo gone, I feel like he has been ripped from me for a second time. For while the pen had signed the adoption papers, my heart had withheld permission. When Mammy found the photo of him, I'd pretended that someone else's had slipped into the envelope in the chemist. For safe keeping I put it in a tin box and buried it at the base of the cherry tree, my buried secret.

How I've been punished for falling head over heels in love with a hunk two years my senior to whom I was nothing more than a passing flutter. Who could possibly have told me that twenty-seven years on, I would still be incarcerated? No release date pending.

When my head is healed, I pen a letter. The reply comes from the adoption agency, he hasn't made contact. Now it's my turn to be rejected. I plant seeds along the wall, in view of the kitchen window. Then I wait, for that's all I'm permitted to do. And through my wait I hope and pray, that things will finally go my way, and he'll search for me.

When the first little shoot makes an appearance, it feels like bringing him out of hiding. I determine to pluck up the courage to have some long overdue conversations, starting with Terry, then Mammy and Bernadette. In the meantime, I write.

IS THAT YOU YONDER?

To never know, how tall you grow;
To never show, and make others glow.
To never have shared, hence no one cared.
To sit and wonder, if that's you yonder?
Convicted of a crime, so you couldn't be mine
Surely, I have done my time, for partaking in
this crime?
Why didn't I fight, for our plight?
Why wasn't I brave, then for you my heart
wouldn't crave?
Guilt tugs at my heart, each time I deny you,
Your part in my family tree, of which you should
be key.
As if by pretending you never were, makes you
not there.
Why did I quake and for the sake,
Of dignity and reputation, I lost something
far greater?
No one warned of the road up ahead,
Starting with shame and ending with pain,
I'd do anything to be back there again,
Refusing, with a mere swipe of a pen,
To give you away, not even for one single day.

Katherine Carroll lives in Celbridge with her husband Mark, three teenage children and beagle called Lily who is delighted to have featured in some of Katherine's writing. She is a member of a writers group, Leixlip Library Writers Group, a great source of encouragement, inspiration and friendship. They published their first anthology in 2017. She writes for adults and children – memoir pieces, short stories, poems and a devotional. 'I have Ireland's Own *to thank for first seeing a story in print when I was runner-up in the Beginners Short Story section of their writing competition'. Since then she has had other pieces of her work published in the* Ireland's Own *magazine.*

Smashed Eggs and Stalin

By Angela McKeon,
Marino, Dublin

A broken egg during the making of a tea brack to her granny's recipe brings back childhood memories of another baking and egg-breaking episode when she was the one helping granny to do the baking …

POPE FRANCIS WAS coming to Ireland for the World Meeting of Families. I was expecting some family home from abroad, so I decided to bake a tea brack in honour of the occasion, using my Granny's old tried and trusted recipe. I steeped the fruit overnight in hot tea and a generous amount of Irish whiskey.

The next morning I set about adding the rest of the ingredients. As I lifted a large brown egg from the bowl, it slipped through my hand and landed with a splat on the kitchen floor. I stood staring at the sticky, sickly mess spreading around my feet. I was transfixed and my mind took me straight back to 1955.

The peony roses always bloomed in time for my birthday, and the 1st May 1955, my fifth birthday, was no exception. I woke to a hazy sunshine slanting across my bed; it shone softly on the patch-work quilt that Granny had made from scraps of material. I could smell the peat fire from downstairs that always burned winter and summer. I wondered if I would get a birthday card or maybe even a present. I jumped up and got dressed quickly, excitement building.

When I rushed into Granny's kitchen, she enveloped me in a huge birthday hug. She smelt of lavender and flour. She then ceremoniously placed a milk bottle on the table and a single perfect pink peony rose peeped out from the bottle. 'There pet,' she said. 'Your own special birthday rose.' I ran my finger along the pink silky petals and reached over to smell its lovely perfume.

The old wireless on the kitchen dresser was on and Fr. Sydney MacEwan was singing *'The Flowers of the May'* and Granny and I sang along. Granny had a lovely voice and she sang in the church choir. I ate porridge laced with honey and cinnamon from my special bowl with blue stripes around the edges. Then Granny asked 'Would you like to collect the eggs?' I jumped into my wellies and went skipping into the yard with the egg basket. I had gathered eight brown eggs when, out of nowhere, Stalin, the aptly named cockerel, came flying at me with wings flapping and squawking very loudly.

I was terrified. I tried to run, but my wellies got stuck in the mud, the basket fell from my hand and I fell on top of it. The yellowy slimy, sticky gloopiness snaked its way under my outstretched hands and made me feel sick.

As I lay there sobbing uncontrollably, Stalin continued to emit a high pitched squawking sound and started to peck at the broken eggs. I was petrified, afraid to move a muscle in case Stalin would peck me. Then, I heard running feet and I was scooped up into the strong, powerful arms of my Grandad. He kicked out at Stalin and said something to him about next Sunday's dinner.

I buried my face in his shoulder as he carried me indoors. Granny was very upset when she saw me and she agreed with Grandad about next Sunday's dinner. After one of Granny's special hugs, she put me sitting on the kitchen table and set about cleaning up my cuts and grazes.

'What will I use for an antiseptic?' asked Granny. She looked at the dresser, the TCP bottle was empty, then her gaze stopped at the bottle of Baby Power whiskey. 'This will have to do,' she said. I saw a look of alarm cross Grandad's face.

When Granny was bathing my cuts with the whiskey, Grandad cut three generous slices of brack and slathered each one with home-made butter. He then made three mugs of tea with plenty of sugar, and, with a wink at me, poured a generous amount of Power's whiskey into his mug.

'For God's sake man,' complained Granny, 'it's still only early morning you know.'

'It's a well-known old remedy for shock,' he replied with a broad smile on his face. Grandad knew everything. 'Trust you to know that kind of information,' retorted Granny, but she was smiling.

The three of us sat sipping our teas and eating the tea brack, with the wireless playing in the background. When Delia Murphy started to sing *'The Spinning Wheel'* Grandad whisked Granny from the chair and started to waltz her around the kitchen. I was enchanted watching them. When the dance was over, we all clapped and Granny said 'What was that in aid of?'

'It's our Granddaughter's birthday,' Grandad said 'and we are celebrating what really matters – FAMILY.'

Angela McKeon is a retired lady living in Dublin with her husband of forty eight years. They have two adult sons and two grandchildren, Jack and Sarah, who are members of Owen's Club *in the* Ireland's Own *magazine. She has written a few short stories, just for her own amusement. This story is the first she has submitted to any publication.*

She is a life-long reader and loves to get lost in a book, and she also likes the theatre and gets to see quite a lot of productions. She enjoys Bridge nights with her sisters and brother and lunches and outings with her friends. She is a member of a singing group; they sing for fun and they laugh as much as they sing and the energy and the feel-good factor in the room are almost tangible.

Tea Leaves

By Liam Hollywood,
Shinn Road, Newry, Co. Down

*Aidan's wife died five years ago and he has been finding it
difficult to come to terms with life without her, but a friendship
had been blossoming with hairdresser, Sally. However, when
she had remarked on the time they had been going out together
and hinted at her vision of the future, he had frozen and
had been unable to respond to her …*

AIDAN WALKED ON through the whispering snow, unmindful of the cold, the numbness inside far more pressing than any numbness outside. He reached the familiar door and carefully tapped his shoes against the step, automatically checking his reflection in the glass. Tallish and broadish, his assessment never changed. 'You'll do for now Brennan,' the voice assured him.

Carefully he stepped inside and made his way up the long aisle; there was his son, Toby, chatting to the few customers at this time in the morning and managing to catch his eye with a cheery wink. Aidan raised his eyebrows in return and went back to hang up his coat. He slowly folded the scarf and shook the snow from his coat, then hung them above the radiator. A place for everything and everything in its place. 'Old habits die hard, Brennan,' the voice mocked.

He shook his head, as he made his way behind the counter, partly in annoyance and partly in acknowledgement of the voice's sentiments. He knew that he had allowed Toby and his wife Ellen to gradually take over running the shop, and when customers now told him he was part of the furniture they were uncomfortably close to the truth.

Toby's voice shook him from his reverie. 'Thought the snow might have kept you in bed this morning?'

'Funny, I thought the same about you, you always were the best sleeper in the family.' Aidan enjoyed the teasing they both shared; he'd realised long ago that this was his substitute for open affection. He could hear his father's voice across the years, telling him to be a man. Old habits did indeed die hard.

As Toby shook his head in mock bewilderment, Aidan moved to the rear of the shop to brew the tea. No tea bags for him and so, as the kettle boiled, he warmed the pot and spooned the tea leaves into it. He knew the kitchen was a temporary sanctuary for Toby would soon be in here teasing and probing about last night's date with Sally.

'You messed things up there Brennan.' As if he really needed reminding that when Sally had remarked on the time they had been going out together and hinted at her vision of the future, he had been unable to respond to her. Her hurried departure, the chair flung back, coat barely on, had drawn glances from some of the other diners but he had remained fixed in his chair, hands squeezing the table so hard that he had almost ripped the cloth.

During the long night of the soul that followed he played the scene over and over but the ending never varied. When Cathy died it was as if he had hit a brick wall and in the five years since he had not found a way to demolish it. 'Maybe you're afraid to hit the wall too hard in case it falls on you and crushes you.' The mockery in the voice annoyed him.

'Do you think I don't know that?' He felt himself redden as the kitchen door swung open to reveal his son's puzzled face. 'Were you talking to someone?'

'Yes, someone with a bit of sense. Me.' He hoped the banter would distract him from the mess he was in.

'Well, here's someone with even more sense than you, if that's possible,' Aidan ignored the gentle sarcasm and then the door swung further open to reveal Sally standing behind Toby.

'I'll leave you two to it, very busy out front.' His son had the decency to blush at the outright lie. Aidan tried to catch Sally's eye but the green eyes he knew and loved looked everywhere but at him. Toby stepped to one side and Aidan couldn't help noticing that he seemed to steer Sally into the room with his hand in the small of her back.

Although she was a few inches shorter than him and much lighter in build, Aidan felt himself almost contract as she came towards him. Yet, her eyes, usually so full of fire, seemed dulled now and she hesitated as if uncertain of how to continue.

Looking as if he was wading through molasses, he made his way to the teapot and poured the cup for her. Lots of milk, no sugar and not too hot. This had been their ritual for over two years now but he felt no contentment in the old familiar pattern.

'Tea?' The offer was of tea, the question was really how are you? and then, how are we?

She took the cup from him, their fingers brushing each other and in that instant, he wanted to throw his cup on the ground, pull her to him and whisper in her ear what she really did mean to him.

'That would be taking a chance Brennan, a chance you might get hurt again and you don't take chances.' The voice tailed off, regret flowing from it.

Sally stood facing him and the sparkle in her eyes lifted his heart, until he saw it was tears that made them glisten.

'Aidan dear, in a way, I regret what happened last night. Our world has changed because I decided that I need a face across the table in the mornings and on the other side of the fire in the evenings.'

'Nothing has changed Sally, I don't want things to change,' the pleading in his voice unnerved him.

'Aidan, last night I so wanted us to be together and I buried my pride and did everything but propose to you. Yet you sat there like a lump of clay. Why?'

He flinched at the raw honesty in her voice. Unable to say how much he feared losing someone again; how his world had fallen apart five years ago and he didn't think he could go on living if it happened again.

'I think the world of you Sally, you must know that,' he knew the words were wrong, before he even spoke them.

'The only thing I hope is that our business contract remains the same. I thank you for that at least. So I'm assuming that you'll be up later for your monthly haircut? I know you don't like changes but one of the girls will do it, not me.' The parting barb struck home exactly as it was meant to.

The door opened almost as soon as it closed and he stepped towards it, hoping it was Sally, hoping everything would be the way it had been. Instead in walked Toby and Ellen. He tried, unsuccessfully, to mask his disappointment. The way that they glanced at each other told him something was out of kilter and his mind raced through the possibilities, one worse than the other.

Toby and Ellen still hadn't spoken and he noticed that while his son looked slightly sheepish Ellen's eyes were almost aflame with an inner joy. 'Take a seat Aidan.' It was Ellen who broke the silence.

Puzzled and a little wary, he decided to play along. 'Are you sure you don't want to check my blood pressure,' he was glad that at this moment they couldn't.

'Aidan dear, we've found we're going to have a vacancy, for a babysitter, God willing.' As usual Ellen got right to the point.

He couldn't speak in case his voice cracked with emotion. Instead he crossed the room and enveloped Ellen in a great bear hug that said everything. Her gentle squeeze back told him she knew how he felt. Breaking away from her he punched Toby playfully on the shoulder and would have tousled his hair if he could have.

Like Ellen, Toby knew that actions spoke louder than words with his father and he playfully returned the punch.

'Ellen, you make sure this fella looks after your every need and I'm here for both of you if you need me.' He knew he was stating the obvious but he had to say something. Toby just shook his head in amusement and turned back toward the shop. Ellen remained and something in the way that she stood made him pause

She spoke as they both watched Toby bustle through the door. 'We'll miss Sally when she goes.' She turned and looked straight at him and he saw the hurt in her eyes. 'Do you really think things can just go on the way they were? Have you that high an opinion of yourself that you believe Sally will be content to keep things this way until you are both in your dotage?'

She stepped towards him and caught him by the arms. 'I don't know how to get through to you, Aidan. I would like my child to have a Grandma, would you not like that too? I hope you know what you're doing ... or rather, not doing.'

She was gone so quickly that he couldn't have responded, even if he'd been able to. 'Brennan, this is a small town, with no secrets. It's not fair on Toby and Ellen, it's not fair on Sally and can't you even see that it's not fair on you?' He'd spent his life trying to be fair to everyone and the voice hit home.

He finally saw that, with or without him, the sun would continue to rise and set and the seasons follow each other. Any chance for happiness should be grasped for the alternative was to endure rather than enjoy life. His father's words came back again, 'Be a man.'

As he carried the tray, with milk, teapot, cups and sugar in with him he saw that Sally had her back to him but he knew that his entrance had been noted. He realised then that he was probably the main topic of conversation today. Undaunted, he began pouring and handing round cups of tea to staff and customers. Any protests were ignored and soon everyone was sipping from a cup and pretending not to study him.

At that point, Julie nodded to him that he was next and he settled comfortably into the seat. With the warm towel around his neck and her fingers teasing his hair, Aidan allowed himself to relax. 'The calm before the storm, Brennan?'

As if on cue Julie began chatting about the mundane things that every hairdresser trots out. But it was when she mentioned the fundraising night for the local football club that he spotted his chance.

'I'll not be going near it, I offered my services and they turned me down.' His voice tone ensured that everyone in the room focused on him.

'Ach Aidan, sure you're a member this years, why did they do that?' Julie took her role as investigative reporter seriously.

'Just because I offered to tell fortunes!'

He let the words hang in the silence and silence there was. Even Sally was staring at him with a tiny crease of puzzlement between her eyes.

'Aidan; I never knew you could do that?' Julie was a believer already.' How do you tell them?'

'Like my father before me and his father before him ... I read the tea leaves.' As soon as it was out it was as if he had signalled the start of a drinking competition. Cups were being emptied at a frightening speed, considering the age of some of the contestants.

'I've only time to do one. Sally can I have your cup?' He wasn't surprised to find that Sally was the only person who hadn't drained her cup, but with everyone looking at her she finished the tea and handed him the cup.

He took it, upturned it on a saucer, and then spun it three times. With a flourish he swept the cup away and appreciated the audible sigh from the spectators. Sitting beside her he reached for her hand and looked from the leaves into her eyes.

'You've seen the two days, Sally, good and bad. I see you're a strong person but you can be gentle and kind to those you love.'

When she dropped her eyes he studied the leaves and spoke again to the hushed room. I spoke before of the past and present but what of the future?'

'I see you with a man,' he continued, as she tried to withdraw her hand but he held on. 'This man has many faults and he has tried your patience but he loves you and would like to spend the rest of his life with you. If you'll have me, Sally?'

The room was about to explode in applause when they all realised she hadn't responded. Aidan stared at the bowed head and his heart sank as she raised it and stared at him with eyes full of tears.

Aidan halted at the front door and tapped his shoes against the steps to knock the snow lodged on them. He checked his appearance in the glass of the door and then made his way up the aisle to where Toby stood waiting. His son smiled at him but before either could speak the door of the chapel opened and in came Sally.

Her plain bridal gown seemed to push light into the dark corners of the building and as she came towards him, the voice spoke again, 'I'm proud of you, Brennan. Look after her and look after yourself.'

As he took Sally's arm and stood in front of the priest, Aidan doubted if he'd be hearing from that particular voice again.

Much later in the day, Toby stood on the hotel steps, with his arm around Ellen, waving goodbye to the happy couple. The reception had been joyous and as the guests drifted in to the hotel, she turned his face towards her with the softest of touches.

'You were thinking of your mother just now, weren't you?'

He almost felt disloyal to the newlyweds admitting it, but he nodded his head, words a problem for him at that moment.

'Sure she could not be anything but happy for him now, I know how much she loved him. Even though there were times he drove her mad with his stubborn streak.' Ellen smiled at the recollection of Cathy shaking her head in exasperation when Aidan's back was turned.

'Don't I know all about it,' the happy memories flooded back to Toby now. 'When he wasn't being stubborn it was, Aidan this and Aidan that. But when she lost patience with him, as soon as he left the room all she ever called him, to me, was Brennan!'

Liam Hollywood is 61 years old, married to Eileen, for almost 40 years, with two sons and a daughter and five grandchildren. He works for a local Housing Association and he enjoys golf and gardening and of course, the Armagh football team. Ireland's Own *was a weekly delight to his parents and indeed, uncles and aunts. That tradition has continued with himself and his brother and sisters.*

The Old Wooden Rocking Cradle

By Kevin McDermott,
Crossabeg, Co. Wexford

*Although I knew the cradle was for a baby, I still had no idea
what it was doing in the corner of our kitchen …*

IT WAS A JANUARY day in 1944, when Jim, my eldest
brother, arrived home driving a horse and sprung cart. He
was sixteen years old at the time and had borrowed the
horse and cart from the local butcher shop where he worked.
The cart even had the butcher's name painted on its sides. I
soon became aware that he was to drive the horse and cart to
my Granny's house and pick up a wooden rocking cradle for
my mother.

Although I was over seven years old I had no idea why my
mother wanted a rocking cradle. I wrapped myself in an old
blanket and sat on the floor of the cart as we started on the
eight-mile journey to Granny's house. It was evening when we
reached our destination and we were welcomed with a large
bowl of Granny's home-made soup.

It was a clear starry night when we started for home with the
cradle, and Granny lit an old storm lamp and gave it to Jim to
tie on the cart for safety reasons. I remember as we trotted
along at a steady pace there were occasions when the horse

fought to regain its feet on the icy patches that were beginning to form on the frosty road surface.

We arrived home safely and the cradle was unloaded and stored in the corner of the kitchen. We didn't have electricity at the time and it was the next day when I had a chance to examine our new piece of furniture closely. It was about four feet long and two feet wide with a rocker fitted underneath back and front. It also had an arch shaped wooden canopy at one end.

The exterior was painted with a brown stain and the interior had been decorated with a blue patterned wallpaper. I squeezed myself into it and started rocking. Faster and faster I rocked back and forth until the cradle overturned throwing me out and I banged my head against the wall. On hearing the crash my mother came running into the kitchen and before I could escape her wrath I had received another couple of thumps to add to the pain in my head.

Although I knew that the cradle was for a baby I still had no idea what it was doing in the corner of our kitchen. About six weeks later, on February 28, 1944, I was told that the local Jubilee Nurse had brought my mother a baby boy in her black bag and his name was Patrick Joseph. Now it all made sense. The cradle was for my new baby brother.

Sleeping peacefully under its wooden canopy, he was now on display for any of the neighbours who dropped in to see the new addition to our family. When Patrick was born my father was away working in England and it would not be until the summer of 1944 that he would see his son for the first time. Unfortunately, my older siblings had also flown the nest and consequently the job of being nursemaid would fall on my young shoulders.

Under the guidance of my mother I spent many long hours trying to rock my baby brother to sleep. These were precious hours when I should have been outside playing with my friends and consequently there were occasions when I became very frustrated. I thought that by rocking the cradle harder and faster my baby brother might fall asleep more quickly.

It didn't help that he always focused his eyes on the small swinging Sacred Heart badge that my mother pinned on the cradle behind his head. I was soon brought to my senses by my mother shouting 'For God's Sake … you're shaking the life out of the poor child.'

She would then take over and by singing softly as she rocked the cradle, the baby was soon asleep. She always choose hymns to sing and my abiding memory is of her softly singing *'Soul of my Saviour'* and *'Hail Queen of Heaven'* as she gently rocked the cradle. My reward for rocking the cradle was to get the very tasty remnants of the boiled baby powder from the saucepan that she used to make his bottle.

When he was about two months old Patrick developed Diphtheria. The doctor wanted to send him into the fever hospital but mother pleaded with him to let her keep him at home one more night. The doctor agreed and I remember that the steam from boiling kettles on the stove was directed under the canopy of the cradle in the belief that it would help the baby to breathe easier. The neighbours sat with my mother all night and many rosaries were recited.

The next day when the doctor called he found a marked improvement in Patrick's health. Thankfully, the crisis had passed. Eventually, my baby brother outgrew the old wooden cradle and it lay unused in our kitchen for a few months before being transported off to the home of a newly married couple where I'm sure it was put to good use.

Kevin McDermott was born in Cavan town; he emigrated to England in 1955 but he returned to Ireland to live in Crossabeg in 1990 with his wife Noreen. They have two sons, James and Ronan. He spent 25 years as a London fire-fighter. He is an accomplished musician, and he enjoys acting and performing comedy recitations. In 2004 he published his autobiography 'The Time of the Corncrake'. *He has recorded a CD of recitations,* 'Many Miles of Potholed Road' *which included three of his own compositions, and to celebrate his 80th birthday in 2016 he recorded a CD of some of his own favourite accordion music called* 'Musical Gems from a Button Box'.

Sojourn in West Clare

By Mae Leonard,
Naas, Co. Kildare

*Novelist Charlotte Bronte and her husband Arthur Bell-Nicholls
spent their honeymoon in Ireland in 1854 and after visiting with
her new in-laws at Banagher, they journey on to Kilkee seaside
resort and spa where she enjoys a romantic and health-improving
sojourn, possibly the happiest time of her life …*

S HE AWAKES AT DAYBREAK to the sound of the
sea. Arthur unlatched the window last night as she had
requested him. She listens to the soothing sigh of each
curving wave. She can smell its salt and the seaweed it carries
and she lies there savouring every moment of this quiet time.
She feels a growing peace within herself. Charlotte closes her
eyes and gives thanks to the Lord for the long, long journey
that brought her to this place.

She thanks Him also for the gift of this tender, patient husband
whom she is learning to love more and more each day. Her
smile widens and she gives thanks for the gift of a full night's
slumber. She slept without any disturbance for the first time in
months. At long last something good is happening in her life.
She raises her left hand and kisses the gold band on her third
finger and asks herself in a whisper:

'What does he see in me to love me thus? I am a plain-faced
woman of such short stature and not in any way elegant. My

hair is unremarkable being neither brown nor auburn but mid-way between. Oh! He, who is my husband, is so strong and so handsome – I am coming to, to love him more every day.'

Arthur stirs next door. She hears the creak of the bed-springs as he sits up, eases himself out of the bed, slides on his slippers and reaches for his dressing gown. He pulls out the chamber pot from the wash stand to do what he has to do. She hears him pour water from the ewer jug into the basin and soaps his hands and face.

Then comes the snip-snip of the little scissors as he trims his beard. 'Such a very male occupation,' Charlotte remarks to herself, still smiling. This is a whole new world to her – a contented life, something that she thought she would never, ever experience. Charlotte thinks of the battle this persistent gentleman had to win her hand in marriage. A year long wait before she would give him an answer to his proposal and then he faced up bravely to her father's fury for daring to suggest that he was a worthy suitor for his daughter.

Why did her father object so fiercely to their enjoinment? Was it because Arthur is Irish? Or perhaps he thought that this suitor had his eye on her good financial standing. Charlotte, in her growing up, somehow gleaned an opinion from her father that all Irishmen were worthless and, indeed, her fortune had increased considerably over the past few years.

Now she wishes that her father could have journeyed back to his own native land with them to see the welcome afforded her at Arthur's family residence in Ireland. And, indeed, he could have feasted his eyes on the great mansion and rich lands they possess. His people are gentry far above her father's station.

Honeymooning at Banagher, it was Arthur's aunt, noticing Charlotte's wan appearance, who suggested that the couple visit Kilkee on the west coast for the healthy benefit of its bracing Atlantic breezes. She had been there on a previous occasion and had been uplifted by the fresh air and the spa baths there.

In Kilkee this morning, Charlotte feels well enough to rise but pauses to allow Arthur his pleasure of administering to her as he has done since their marriage last month. He has been so attentive that she feels somewhat guilty but she still enjoys this new situation, this concerned tenderness that he so selflessly affords her.

'Dearest,' he addresses her in a whisper, lest she be still sleeping, on opening the adjoining door. His face lights up on seeing her smile. 'You're awake, my love!' She reaches out a hand to him, 'Come.' He moves to her bedside, a puzzled look on his face. Her eyes sparkle. 'Come.' She repeats, 'Come join me.' And she throws back the heavy eiderdown. She notes the concern in his eyes but assures him that now she feels well enough to share their love.

A half-hour or so later there is a timid knock on the bedroom door. 'Yes?' Arthur asks sharply. 'The Missus wants to know if ye'll be having yer breakfast now.'

Arthur looks at his bride's smiling face and she nods. 'Yes.' He shouts, 'We'll be down in fifteen minutes or so.' And the two newly-weds giggle like young children.

Kilkee in the West of Ireland is one of the prettiest spa resorts in the British Isles. Charlotte and Arthur sit before the bow window in the dining room of The West End Hotel to enjoy breakfast of mackerel, fried eggs, thick slices of bacon and brown soda bread. They eat heartily and discuss their plans for the day.

Every now and then they pause to admire the scene presented before them, the horseshoe shape of beach, the pale sand and the line of bathing boxes along the sea wall. There are high cliffs on both sides enclosing the bay, the west side is Dunlickey and the east end promontory is named St. George's Head.

Their contemplation is interrupted by the arrival of Jane, daughter of Mrs. Shannon, the proprietor of The West End Hotel. 'Begging your pardon Ma'am and Mister. Curly Mick Mahon will be trying out his new horse on the strand before twelve. He's running at the point-to-point in Newmarket-on-Fergus the morrow. Ye might like to see him run.'

Arthur looks at his wife, she smiles broadly and that is sufficient for him to say, 'Thank you Jane, perhaps we might stroll down there later.'

Jane does not recognise that she is being dismissed and she continues. 'And Ma'am, the old gypsy woman will be coming by here for the Fair of Garland Sunday and if you so wish I could take you to her to have your fortune read in the lines of your hand.'

'Jane!' Her mother calls sharply standing at the open dining room door, 'Don't be interfering with our guests. Return to the kitchen at once, there's plenty for you to do there.'

Mrs. Shannon pauses whilst the girl eases past her then goes on, 'Madam, Sir, I am heartily sorry for the inconvenience that Jane may have caused you. She is full of nonsense and flights of fancy. I'm sure a walk up the road by the cliffs at Dunlickey would be far more of benefit to your health and ...'

'Thank you so much Mrs. Shannon,' Charlotte interrupts, 'We are discussing our plans for the day. Please bring us some more tea and some of your delicious brown bread.'

A smile lights up Charlotte's eyes as she turns to her husband. 'It is such a lovely morning, let us try the cliff walk, Arthur dear, shall we?' She speaks his name hesitantly, unused to addressing him thus. But there is a breathless softness in the way she enunciates it. She blushes at such boldness and the sudden gush of emotion within her on saying his Christian name. He was always addressed as Mr. Bell-Nichols when he visited Haworth.

Later, her husband is only too happy to comply with her wishes but fusses about her, insisting that she wear a shawl and he also carries a woollen travel-rug should she have need of it. They make their way up the narrow path on the stony incline and, with some difficulty; clamber down onto the flat rock surface jutting out over the sea. This warm July day Charlotte is charmed by the wild flowers surviving in the crevices of the cliff face despite being dampened by salt sea-spray and tossed in wild Atlantic breezes.

'I must sit here for a while,' she tells her husband and he bows to her wish by finding a sheltered place and folding the rug for her to sit upon. He smiles and nods and takes himself away so that she can have the peace and quiet that Charlotte requires. Below her the Atlantic battles with the long arms of the Duggerna Rocks. The scent of new-mown hay hangs on the air to mingle with that of peat smoke from little cottage hearths. Seagulls squawk overhead, curlews call a warning of the rain to come and a school of dolphins ploughs through the turquoise water to delight the watcher. Charlotte is breathless in admiration.

There is rain the next day as the curlews predicted. Arthur reads his book in the parlour whilst Charlotte writes to her friend Catherine Wooler. Dating her letter, Friday 14th July, 1854, she tells of walking the cliffs and being delighted by the wild Atlantic beating against them. She tells of her growing love for her husband and of his gentle attentiveness to her without intruding on her quiet times.

Charlotte writes: 'So far he is always good in this way and this protection, which does not interfere or pretend, is I believe a thousand times better than any half sort of pseudo sympathy.'

Arthur also writes to a friend telling him of their journey down the Shannon River by boat, then travelling by coach onto Kilkee describing it as '... a glorious watering place with the finest shoreline I have ever saw completely girded with stupendous cliffs ...'

After the rain there comes a day of great calmness. The sun is warm. The sea is smooth as glass and little wavelets turn onto the strand with hardly a sound. Charlotte and Arthur sit outside the West End Hotel watching the ritual of bathers below them. The bathing boxes, on wheels, are pulled by a pony out into the sea. At a certain point they are halted and ladies emerge dressed in all-covering bathing suits so that they may bathe modestly away from prying eyes. Men are not allowed in the area during the ladies' allocated bathing time.

The honeymooners prefer taking their walks together up the cliffs on both sides of the village. Each day Charlotte feels that she is becoming stronger and healthier. The cough that had been bothering her recently seems to have abated and she enjoys the attentions of her husband both in and outside of the bed chamber.

'Arthur, dear, let us remain a little longer in the place.'

He looks a bit doubtful saying, 'We should visit Banagher once more before we return to England.'

'Must we?'

Arthur bites his lip as he ponders his wife's request for a moment or two. She watches him with pleading eyes. 'No.' He says firmly, having made up his mind. He must look after this delicate creature despite upsetting or even insulting his family. 'We may dally here for a week or so then perhaps journey across the Shannon and down along the Atlantic coastline southwards for a few more days. Yes, my love, we will remain here now if that is what you wish.'

109

Charlotte Bronte found love and healing, both physically and mentally, whilst on honeymoon in Kilkee, Co. Clare that July in 1854. Arthur Bell-Nichols was proving to be exceptionally good for her. Soon they would return to her father and the harsh regime at Haworth but she now felt a new energy stirring within her.

A miracle? She died seven months later of 'a pregnancy related illness.'

Mae Leonard now lives in Naas, Co. Kildare, but is a native of Limerick and that city features in many of her stories and recollections, which have been published in many outlets. She has appeared regularly in the Ireland's Own *anthologies and is a regular contributor to* Ireland's Own *magazine and the iconic* Sunday Miscellany *on RTE radio on Sunday mornings.*

'My Lady in the Gabardine Coat'

By Margaret Sheriff,
Gorey Hill Upper, Co. Wexford

*Working on a Female Medical Ward and being the most junior
trainee, my job consisted mostly of cleaning and this was how
I was introduced to her, the person I began to call 'My Lady'
in my head. 'Good morning Nurse' she'd say, a broad
smile reaching her eyes. I blushed each time she said that
because, despite the uniform, I didn't feel like a nurse.*

I DON'T REMEMBER her name but she always stands
behind and to the left of me. She wears a black, belted
gabardine coat; she's tall, grey haired and angular. In
reality I never saw her in a gabardine coat, only in a night-
gown, but that's how she presents to me now over forty years
later. I constantly feel her presence watching and guiding me.

I was eighteen and a first year student nurse, struggling in
a system that was authoritarian and hierarchical, with little
regard for softness, and could be cruel and unsupportive. It was
not what I had expected and I was lonely for home. My legs
and back ached from the sheer physicality of the work.

Working on a Female Medical Ward and being the most
junior trainee, my job consisted mostly of cleaning and this
was how I was introduced to her, the person I began to call
'My Lady' in my head.

The morning smells in the sluice room where I began each day assaulted my senses and I was always glad to get onto the main ward to clean. She was in the last bay of the ward; I admit, I'd rush through the other patients to get to her bed.

'Good morning Nurse' she'd say, a broad smile reaching her eyes. I blushed each time she said that because, despite the uniform, I didn't in any way feel like a nurse. Over the course of days as I cleaned around her bed frame and locker we got talking. She asked about my family and my life and told me snippets about hers.

Her husband had died some years previously and she had two adult sons living in England who rarely contacted her. She told me of the loneliness of her life and how she missed the busy early years of family, especially now she was sick with heart disease.

'I've a broken heart' she'd say and I think I understood what she meant.

I confided in her I didn't think I'd really make a nurse.

'Stick with it; you'll make a great nurse' she encouraged me. 'The early years of anything new are always the hardest.'

One evening when the Ward Sister berated me for a spelling mistake in front of a ward full of visitors, My Lady's intense blue eyes latched onto mine willing the tears that were about to spill to remain unshed. Later on she comforted me as I tried to come to terms with my embarrassment.

'Don't listen to her,' she encouraged. 'Never let anyone else make you feel bad through their ignorance.' We giggled when I confided in her the nickname for the sister was 'The Jennet'.

'She's a right auld ass alright,' she laughed.

She squeezed my hand and looking directly at me said, 'I never had a daughter, but if I had, I'd want her to be just like you.' I found such comfort in her support.

I arrived at her bedside a few mornings later; she was sitting up brushing her hair. 'Would you help me out to the bathroom please Nurse?' she asked. I was delighted to help. I gently swung her legs to the side of the bed, then, placed my hands under her arms to lift her. She looked up at me smiling and whispered 'Thank you.'

The depth of colour in her blue eyes pierced mine. Then it happened; her head slumped forward as I physically felt the life-force leave her body and spread up my arms. Her body went limp as I shouted for help. I carefully lay her back on the pillows and whispered a fervent Act of Contrition in her ear, but, my prayers could not contain the life in her.

More experienced staff arrived and I was hushed away to continue dusting as I fought back the tears.

A few hours later she had disappeared and her bed washed, aired and ready for a new occupant.

That night in bed I cried; for My Lady, myself, and my first introduction to death. How brutal and sudden it was, yet how gentle and quiet. I barely knew her, yet, shared one of the most intimate moments of her life; her death.

In all the years since passed, she remains with me and I wonder who she was. She comes to me as comfort in moments of sadness and raises my spirit and I feel her presence.

I did complete my training and, as she promised, it did get easier. Over a long working life I've been privileged to be with many people at the beginning and end of life and many life changing events between; but, she was the first. She was my mother, my sister, my friend, my lady in the black gabardine coat, and our souls connected.

Margaret Sheriff lives in Gorey, and is married, with an adult family. She trained as a General Nurse and Midwife in the 1970s. She still works fulltime but not at nursing, having been in the Education system for over twenty years; she co-ordinates the Gorey School Completion Programme, where different supports and interventions are offered to help keep young people in school. She has always been interested in writing and many years ago had a few pieces published in Ireland's Own *and other publications, but work and family life took over and writing had to take a back seat. Retirement beckons and she hopes to get more involved in writing again.*

Open Doors

By Richard Lysaght,
Walkinstown Road, Dublin

*Nora feels very much put upon and taken for granted by
her sister-in-law who wants to off-load her moody teenage
daughter, Sophie, for the weekend while she and her husband
jet off to Paris. This prospect does not fill Nora with
any great joy, but she feels she can't refuse …*

NORA SAT WITH her fingers gripping the arms of the armchair. Two hours hoovering, dusting, polishing and changing bedclothes had done nothing to ease Nora's anger at her sister-in-law, Susan. 'I have a good mind to ring Susan and say that the old folks have asked me to help out at the weekend, as they are short staffed.'

Of course, there was no way Nora would do such a thing; to do so would be both underhand and sneaky. Still, as Nora's eyes gazed at her mobile phone on the coffee table, the words, 'hasn't Susan been underhand and sneaky with me?' slipped past her lips.

She replayed the earlier conversation with Susan in her mind. 'I suppose you will helping out in the old folks home at the weekend or else going out dancing,' Susan said in an airy voice.

'No, this weekend I'm just resting. I'll finish work on Friday, lunchtime, and after that, putting the feet up and watching some musical DVDs is about as exciting as it's going to get. I'm afraid my dancing days are past, haven't got the energy now.'

Nora's lips tightened into a line. 'Why was I so stupid? I should have known that Susan was fishing, making sure I'd be here.' She shook her head. 'Susan's just like the crowd in work, always wanting me to do something for them. Oh, Nora, as you're going out would you bring me back a latte and a blueberry muffin, if you don't mind.'

'Well as you have nothing special on,' Susan's words taunted her, 'is there any way you could possibly take Sophie? You see, Michael and I have a chance of a weekend away in Paris, and we are stuck with what to do with her. We have asked her to come, but you know the way they are at sixteen, or nearly seventeen, as she constantly reminds me. Going anywhere with your parents, even being seen with them, is totally uncool. God give me strength!'

'And, unfortunately, her friends just happen to be away this very weekend, wouldn't you know. I really would love, just love, to see Paris. Never been, suppose you have?'

Before Nora could say 'No,' Susan added, 'It would mean so much to us and it is only for three days. We're going Friday morning and we'll be back Monday evening around seven. You could send Sophie home Monday afternoon, if you like, and she'll be company for you, if nothing else.'

From the way Susan said 'company for you,' Nora felt that she was ninety instead of forty.

'And she won't be any bother,' Susan went on. 'Been a bit moody of late, going around with earphones on her head all the time, but take no notice, they're all moody and messy so-and-sos at that age.'

Nora's heart quickened, the images of scattered clothes, unwashed dishes, lids off jars (unthinkable with so many flies about in the hot weather), sending shivers of alarm pulsing through her.

'But what does she like to eat?' Nora said, determined that she would make sure to do all the cooking herself and lessen the chance of a mess being left.

'Chinese food, she loves it. Sometimes I think we were given the wrong child to take home.'

'Chinese, but I can't cook Chine …'

'Oh, don't let that worry you,' Susan said and laughed. 'I can assure you the only Chinese food she gets here is from Mister Wongs takeaway, and that is a rare treat. No, she eats what we eat, not that she eats very much. Watching her weight, God help us. John says he's seen more weight on a ghost but no point in telling her that, won't listen.'

Susan laughed again and then said, 'God, better go, so much to do. John says you'd think we were going for a month. But I told him we women have our needs, haven't we?'

'Yes,' Nora mumbled.

'So, is it alright if she goes over to you on Friday afternoon?'

'Yes, I suppo…'

'Great, you're an absolute diamond. Knew John and I could depend on you. And, by the way, I was saying to John that you should really visit more often. We only ever get to see you at the Christmas and maybe once during the year. Really not good enough, you know. Birdy must fly, hugs and kisses all round.'

Nora eased her grip on the chair, leaned back, and closed her eyes. 'So much for having a quiet weekend.' She sighed, keeping her eyes closed. 'Just wish I didn't feel so tired. Must be getting old. Oh, to be twenty-five again or to even feel like twenty-five.' Memories of going out dancing four nights a week – 'The Imperial' was her favourite haunt – swirled in her brain. Moments later she found herself humming Abba's *Dancing Queen*, her body swaying.

She smiled, the image of a six-foot man with black hair, and wearing a shirt festooned with red parrots, appearing in front of her. She saw herself staring in disbelief at the shirt, a shirt that definitely belonged to someone getting on a plane bound for Hawaii.

'Oh, my mother got it for me,' he said, inclining his head towards her so as she could hear him above the music.

She laughed, catching the slightly musky scent of his deodorant, which she found she liked.

'Will I ask her to get you one?' he said, an impish smile on his face, a roguish glint in his eyes.

'No, thanks, you're fine,' she said, putting her hand up to her mouth in an attempt to hide her laughter.

She laughed again now at the memory, and for a few moments a lightness and joy spread through her, spawning the urge to get up and dance, and then her heart pounded. She opened her eyes, sat upright in the chair, her breathing coming in gasps.

'What am I doing, thinking of Pearce?' She knew from past experience never to dwell on disturbing thoughts, best always to keep busy. She scanned the room for something she might have missed, but even the plastic flowers in the copper coloured pot in the corner of the room held a dull sheen, as did the cornice running round the edge of the ceiling, while everything else twinkled and glittered, catching the sun streaming through the window, in acknowledgement of her lavish attention.

She groaned, more thoughts of Pearce teasing her. 'Stop it,' she said, 'I have enough to be thinking about how I am going to keep Sophie amused.' Nora sprang to her feet; the sudden thought to change the yellow duvet with the grey floral design she had put on Sophie's bed to a more neutral plain duck-egg blue, banishing the disturbing thoughts.

Sophie arrived late on Friday afternoon, hugged Nora and said, 'is it alright if I go to my room, I'm a bit wrecked.'

'Of course,' Nora said, 'just let me know when you want something to eat.'

'Already had something, am stuffed.'

Nora watched her traipse up the stairs. 'Black hair, black jeans, black tee-shirt, and a black backpack in flitters; I have seen brighter shadows.' Still the backpack gave her an idea.

Next morning after breakfast, Nora asked, 'Would you like go to town and pick out a new backpack? The one you have, I think, has had its day.'

'No, thanks, Aunt Nora, think I'll just crash for the day and listen to some music.'

'Did you not sleep?' Nora said, noticing the red puffy eyes.

'Not great.'

'Well, okay then, you rest and maybe tomorrow we can go into town.'

Sophie nodded, and disappeared upstairs.

Nora spent the morning browsing the local shopping centre. In the afternoon she attempted to sit and watch *Oklahoma*, her faourite musical, but her attention kept wandering to Sophie.

'She's hardly still asleep?' Nora glanced at her watch, nearly five-o-clock. 'I think I'll check that she's alright and see if she's hungry.'

Nora knocked lightly on the door and hearing no response turned the handle.

Sophie sat with her back facing the door, shoulders hunched, her hands holding something in them. A pair of headphones covered her ears and the words of the song 'I will always love you' reached Nora as she stepped closer to the bed.

'Sophie,' Nora called twice, louder the second time, before Sophie turned and looked at her with watery eyes. Nora glanced down, glimpsed the front of a photograph before Sophie flipped it over, and placed it on the bed beside her.

'Boyfriend trouble?'

Sophie nodded.

Nora sat beside her and said, 'Do you mind if I have a look?'
Sophie handed her the photo.

A fresh-faced looking boy sat on a black motorbike with high handlebars.

Memories of Pearce swarmed in Nora's brain. The boy had the same roguish look in his eyes as Pearce. 'Have an argument with him?' Nora said.

'Found out he was going with another girl behind my back.' Sophie said, her voice brittle.

'Oh, I know what that's like,' Nora said, not meaning to.

'You do?' Sophie said, looking at Nora and sniffling.

'Afraid so.'

'Did you love him?'

'Yes, very much, and I thought he loved me. We talked about getting married.'

'No way.'

Nora nodded. 'Even looked at hotels we might book.'

'What happened?'

'He went to live in Canada.'

'Why didn't you go with him?'

'He never asked me.'

'You're joking!'

'Afraid not. Didn't even tell me. Just sent a letter saying he was too much of a free spirit to settle down, but that I would always be the sparkle in his heart.' Nora shook her head. 'A year later he married a girl he had been seeing while he was with me.'

'Oh, that's awful. You must have been in right bits.'

'For a long time, but you have to get on with living your life even when it is painful, don't you?'

'I suppose,' Sophie said and then added, 'You ever think of him now?'

'Odd time. It's like walking down a corridor with doors and one of them is slightly open and though you know there is nothing behind it, you can't help but take the occasional peek in when you pass.'

'That's sad,' Sophie said, and leaned her head onto Nora's shoulder. 'I don't know how I'd cope if someone did that to me,' Sophie said, pressing even closer to Nora.

'All you can do is open some other doors and hope for better behind them.'

'Is that what you did, aunt Nora?'

The temptation to say yes bristled within Nora, but the words refused to leave her lips. She shook her head and said, 'No, I didn't, Sophie. I was too afraid, afraid of getting hurt, of being made a fool of again.' Her breath caught, 'I just rushed past.'

'Oh, God, you must have been hurt really bad.' Sophie said, placing her arm around Nora's waist.

Nora wrapped her arm around Sophie's shoulders and she hugged her.

'I guess, I was,' Nora said and became quiet. For the next few minutes, Nora thought of how she had spent the last fifteen years, since Pearce, cocooned in her own safe world, a world that alternated between work and home. Tears rolled down her face, and thoughts of regret filled her mind. She neither dried the tears nor tried to banish the thoughts.

Later, when the tears stopped and the thoughts slunk away, she stood up, kissed Sophie on the top of the head and said, 'I think it's time we had something to eat?'

Sophie nodded and then said, 'Aunty Nora, thanks for telling me what happened to you and for not saying that I am silly to be crying over some fellah at my age.'

'Affairs of the heart are never silly, at any age.' Nora said, and then added, 'What do you say, shall we both go out to a Chinese restaurant?'

'That'd be deadly. You like Chinese food?'

'Let you know later.' Nora smiled, striding out of the room. It was time to start opening doors.

Richard Lysaght has been writing for as long as he can remember, often short stories with a ghostly and supernatural flavour to them, and has had quite a few accepted for publication. He had a children's novel, Black Bag Mystery, *published some years ago and he has also finished a novel, which sadly didn't turn out as he had hoped it would. He is rewriting it from a different angle. He is also tinkering with some ideas for a science fiction novel and endeavouring to make inroads in the ever expanding pile of books he wants to read. He was runner-up in the* Ireland's Own *Short Story Competition in 2016/17 with* Talking with my Father. *He retired after working for An Post for more than thirty years. He has three children and four grandchildren, who keep him physically active and mentally alert.*

My Potato Cupboard

By Barbara Jones,
Newhaven, East Sussex, England

My Nan used her cupboard under the stairs to store her potatoes, and it held a particular fascination for me as a child and every time I visited her, I just had to have a sniff around in it, a small ritual I was compelled to perform.

MY NAN ALWAYS kept her potatoes in a cupboard beneath the stairs. A funny place to store them by today's standards, alongside all the modern paraphernalia of electric carpet washers, paint rollers, etc. that we use ours for, but as a child I didn't question why adults did certain things.

That cupboard of hers held a particular fascination for me and every time I visited her, I just had to have a sniff around in it, a small ritual I was compelled to perform. Mum and Nan would usually stand chatting in the front room and my Nan would pretend she didn't know I was desperately waiting to sniff her cupboard.

The pretence was dragged out as she spoke and laughed with my mother. I would hang about waiting to be noticed, and she would carry on pretending not to see me. Then, Nan would edge toward the cupboard, little by little, in a teasing sort of way. Her hand reaching out resting on the doorknob, while I would almost burst waiting for that 'turn'.

She tantalised me, standing there giggling, her hand on the doorknob, not turning it and laughing her asthmatic, crackly laugh, rocking about, watching me squirm.

This taunting continued, until she'd say, in her Irish brogue, 'So, what is it ye want? Now let me see.'

She knew jolly well what I wanted, but she just enjoyed delaying things and having a laugh as I waited patiently to get into her smelly old cupboard.

'I want to sniff the cupboard,' I'd reply, always falling for the same trap.

'Oh, so ye want to get into this old cupboard do ye?'

'Yes.'

'So, in ye go,' she'd laugh and would thrust the door open where all the treasures were revealed. I was the only one who performed this ritual, and it was mine alone.

I'd experience exhilaration beyond words as I tumbled towards that dark doorway and the musty smell; I'd feel a cool dankness – my eyes slowly adjusting to the darkness of it.

Forward I would creep into the darkness until my whole body was curled up foetus-like in the gloom.

'Will I close the door?' Nan would ask. And I would sit watching her. Sometimes I liked it closed, or would ask her to leave it open. It depended on how I felt and then I'd sit there sniffing. All the smells of her understairs cupboard meant everything to me at five. This was my own private world.

Most of the potatoes had dry crumbly mud clinging to their skins, but some had wet slippery soil stuck to the fork holes where my Nan had dug them up. Wet and slippery, dry and dusty, I loved to smell them all.

I would run my fingers over the lumpy shapes, my thumbs investigating each and every crevice until I felt I had taken stock of her potatoes. Sometimes they would be on the 'turn'. These had their own smell that was unique, a different decaying, decomposing aroma that I learned to separate from the good ones. When I pushed my finger into the decaying mass it squelched and a horrible smell ran out leaving my intruding finger black and smelling of putrefaction.

This was the icing on the cake. To find a squelchy, squashy one was the ultimate pleasure. Pushing in a finger to feel the organic mass caving in beneath my power was like re-shaping the world. I could make things happen. I could squash potatoes, or just leave them there for Nan to find, all rotting and smelly.

Sometimes I would pick out these rotting potatoes and give them to her, so that she wouldn't need to crawl into the cupboard herself. I think she was glad of this help.

Once satisfied that there had been enough sniffing, I would emerge needing no other entertainment all day, except perhaps a visit to the chickens to smell their straw and look for eggs. This farmyard smell in the middle suburbia was the closest thing to heaven for me.

Now when I have bought farm potatoes and I reach into my cupboard to take one out, the memory of that particular smell floods my mind. I close my hand over the potato and see her hand simultaneously reaching out, folding around the door-knob of her potato cupboard and we touch in that single act. Memories of her laughter followed by an eerie silence and emptiness inside.

My hand grips the potato as I remember her death, and all the toys of my world breaking. I breathe her again; recapturing memories that are as far away and as untouchable as the stars.

Barbara Jones was born and grew up in London but moved to Sussex where she graduated from University of Sussex in Natural Sciences. She taught Science for a while but moved into industry as typesetting became computerised. She and her husband purchased a ramshackle house for holidays in France, which they renovated, and it's there she has done most of her writing. She is a grandmother and a great grandmother, but never forgets her Irish ancestry of which she is proud.

The Writing Class

By Linda Lewis,
Exeter, Devon, England

*I had been persuaded to sign up for my first creative writing class;
it would be good therapy, I was assured. Now I was actually
sitting in the classroom for the first time it no longer seemed like
such a good idea. I could have been five again, facing my first
day at school and I was about to turn tail and run ...*

B Y THE TIME I arrived at the college for my first creative
writing class, my nerves were at breaking point. I might be
sixty-one, but walking into a room full of strangers has
never been my favourite thing to do. I peered anxiously through
the doorway. I was a good ten minutes early, but the room was
already full of competent and intelligent looking ladies, all of
whom looked to be at least twenty years older than me.

They were all chatting away, nineteen to the dozen. A cold
trickle of fear ran down my back. I was about to turn tail and run,
when a kindly soul spotted me.

'Come and sit by me,' she said.

'Thanks.'

'I'm Mabel.'

I was just about to introduce myself when a woman walked
into the room. She looked to be around my age, mid-thirties, but
something told me this wasn't another pupil. Everything about
her oozed confidence. As she took her place at the front of the
class, a hush spread round the room like ripples from a stone
dropped into a pond.

'Welcome everybody. It's good to see so many old faces. My name's Janet Wilkins, and I'm your tutor for the next term. For those of you who are new here, there's nothing to worry about. Creative writing doesn't hurt, at least not very much.'

Only one person laughed – me. I guessed it was probably an old joke.

'Right,' said Janet as she emptied her brief case of several files and arranged them on the table in front of her. 'Let's start by introducing ourselves. As we go round the room, tell us your name, and why you've joined a creative writing class.'

My mind shot off on a mission. Why WAS I there? It wasn't because I thought I could write. Joining the class had been my neighbour's idea. I'd been devastated when I lost my wife. Dora said that writing things down just might help me. Dora called it writing therapy.

At first, I dismissed the idea; I have trouble writing a shopping list, but as time passed and I didn't feel much better, I decided to give it a go.

Now I was actually sitting in the classroom it no longer seemed like such a good idea. I could have been five again, facing my first day at school. Everything looked, sounded and smelled completely alien. With an increasing sense of desperation, I tried to figure out what to say while I listened to the others. They weren't having any trouble.

'Hi. I'm Ann. I've been writing for years. Nothing published, but I enjoy it.'

'My name's Kathy. I joined the class because I'd like to write a family history some day.'

By the time it was my turn, my mind had gone completely blank. I said my name and stopped.

The tutor waited for me to continue and when nothing was forthcoming she nodded to encourage me to go on, but I couldn't think of anything to say.

After an agonizing silence, I came out with this gem. 'I'm here because there's nothing much on TV on a Wednesday evening.'

Somebody laughed, provoking a frown from the tutor.

'Welcome anyway,' she said, and moved on to the next person.

When all the introductions were over, the tutor once again addressed the class.

'As most of you know, I believe in jumping straight in. I'd like you to spend five minutes writing about your last holiday.' She checked her watch. 'Starting, now!'

I picked up my pen and stared at the empty page.

My last holiday. She couldn't have picked a worse subject. It was when we were on holiday in Cyprus that I first realised my wife was ill, and that she'd been trying to hide it to save me from worrying about her. Three months later, she passed away.

I looked at Mabel, who was sitting beside me. Her head was bowed as she wrote at a furious pace. Her pen was literally racing across the page. Some of the others were chewing their pencils or staring into space, but gradually inspiration struck and they started writing until I was the only one not scribbling.

'Time's up,' the tutor called at last.

At once a murmur of anticipation filled the room.

'Right,' said Janet. 'Let's go round the class and read what we've written. If you don't want to read, you don't have to, but the point of this class is to share our work so we can learn from each other.'

I was relieved when she started at the front, but after the first row, she skipped to the back.

All too soon her penetrating gaze was on me.

'You're new,' she said with a smile, 'so this probably feels scary, but we're a friendly class. Nobody's going to say anything nasty. So, what did you write?'

'Nothing.'

She tried not to frown but failed. 'Nothing', she said? 'Not even a paragraph?'

'Not a word. Sorry,' I said.

'Never mind. Hopefully the next exercise will be more your cup of tea.' With that she moved on to the next person and I could breathe again.

I'm no judge of what's good or bad as far as writing is concerned, but everything the others had written sounded brilliant. Some were sad, some were so funny, everyone laughed. I could never manage that.

Fortunately, the next part wasn't practical. The tutor read the beginning of one of her own stories and then talked about the importance of getting the first paragraph right.

She called it the hook. 'It's the part that catches the reader's attention so that they want to read on and find out what happens next,' she explained.

She made it sound so simple, only I knew it wasn't. That's when I decided that my joining the class was a mistake. If I left at the break, I might be able to join a different one, maybe something less daunting like beginners' French. I'd never fit into the group. Everyone was so much better than me. They'd obviously been coming to the class for years.

When we broke for refreshments I followed everyone downstairs to the coffee machine. People started to gather into small groups, catching up on each other's news. People were talking about their families, and showing each other photos. It appeared that, apart from me, they were all grandmothers – proud of it too.

I found a seat close to the door, so that I could slip out when the time came.

To my dismay, the tutor came and sat next to me. 'Don't leave,' she said.

'What do you mean?' I said, innocently.

Janet smiled. 'I know you're planning to sneak off. It's written all over your face.'

I opened my mouth to tell her she had it all wrong, but there was no point. I've never been very good at lying. 'You're right,' I admitted. 'I should never have come along in the first place. I have never written anything longer than a complaint letter since I left school.'

'So?'

'Everybody else in the class is so good. They're all miles better than me.'

Her eyes twinkled. 'I'd like to say that's because I'm a great teacher, but it isn't that at all. The fact is, everyone enjoys the classes, and that comes out in their writing.'

'Exactly, which is why I will never be able to do it. When you asked us to write about our recent holidays, my mind went completely blank.'

She looked at me so intently, it felt as though she was reading my mind. 'Did it really,' she said, 'or did you think of something but decide not to put it down on paper? I'm guessing your last holiday wasn't happy. Maybe you thought, I can't write about that, it's too depressing, but that's the joy of writing. You can make things up, take something sad and make it funny. It's really great therapy.'

'That's what my neighbour told me, but look at me. I'll never fit in.'

'It's because you're different that I'd really like you to stay.' She put her hand on my arm. 'I've been teaching this class for three years, and it's starting to get a bit stale. We really need some fresh blood.' She finished her coffee and stood up. 'So, will you stay to the end of the class?'

'I'm not sure.'

She smiled. 'What kind of books do you like?'

'Crime usually,' I admitted.

'Say you'll stay, and I'll see what I can do,' she said.

I'm glad I did, because Janet spent the rest of the lesson talking about crime fiction, then set us an exercise, writing about a murder. That meant I could let my imagination run riot and make things up which was much more my cup of tea. Some of the others struggled which made me realise that trying something new was hard for everyone.

I decided to stay for the rest of the term. I knew my writing wasn't very good, but my neighbour was right, getting it all down on paper really did help. I started to see that the future was not just a blank space, it was something I could look forward to. By the end of term, I was hooked. I could hardly wait for the new one to begin.

On the first night of the spring term, a new lady came along. I spotted her, standing in the doorway, deciding whether to come in or not. She was about my age, maybe a bit younger.

My heart went out to her. I knew just how she felt so I went and had a word with her.

'Don't worry, you'll be fine,' I said.

'Thanks, but I'm not sure I should be here,' she whispered but she followed me inside.

At the break, I bought her a coffee and stayed close by so that she couldn't run away. At the end of the class, I took her to one side. 'You're thinking about not coming again, aren't you, Sue?'

'How did you know?' she asked, her eyes wide.

I smiled. 'I was exactly the same. When I joined the class, I'd never done any writing in my entire life, I was sure I'd never fit in, but I was wrong. It gets easier, but you have to give it time.' I scribbled my telephone number on a piece of paper and gave it to her. 'If you get cold feet, call me.'

When she didn't phone, I half expected her not to turn up for the next class, but she did.

During the break, she thanked me. 'If you hadn't spoken to me last week, I wouldn't have come back.' She grinned. 'As it is, I'm having a great time.'

'My pleasure,' I said.

Week by week, Sue's confidence grew and her writing steadily improved. It wasn't just my opinion either. Everyone said how well she was doing.

At the end of term, the tutor organised a short story competition. The prize was only a book token, even so, the atmosphere as we waited for the result was electric. I knew I wouldn't win, it was enough that I'd finished a story.

When Janet announced that Sue had won first prize, her face lit up. As she walked to the front of the class to claim her prize, she blew me a kiss, and everybody cheered.

Thank goodness I took my neighbour's advice. Writing wasn't just great therapy, it had changed my life. Not only had the pain gone, I'd fallen in love again, something I never expected to happen. I'd found Sue, the woman I wanted to spend the rest of my life with.

I was still the only man in the class, but I wasn't alone any more.

Linda Lewis has been writing short stories for a living since 2003. So far she has sold more than 700 stories to magazines in the UK, Scandinavia and Australia as well as to Ireland's Own. *She has also written several books, most of them designed to help other writers find ideas and improve their craft. Other books include a novel and short story collections, the most recent of which is called* Saving Sam and Other Dog Tales. *Despite writing hundreds of romantic stories, she remains single. She lives in Exeter, in Southwest England where she is building a garden from scratch. Her hobbies include singing, listening to music of all kinds, growing vegetables and painting portraits of animals and people. You can follow Linda on twitter @writingiseasy.*

Maggie's Man

By Brian Donaghy,
Pennyburn Court, Derry

Maggie was a memorable character who often visited our house at night when we were children on our summer holidays in Donegal. She had lots of stories about those she had known over the years. We always joked that turf smoke was her only perfume for we were aware of it as soon as she visited us.

MAGGIE WAS AN old 'residenter' who often called in for a ceili (visit) at night time when we were children in Donegal on our summer holidays. She lived alone and was a recognised seanachí, and many a story had she, mostly of oul characters she'd known thereabouts down the years. Often the conversation centred around her neighbours.

She herself was indeed a memorable character. A battered little tobacco snuff box was her constant companion; battered it may have been but it had served her well for many a year and she never left it out of her hand. 'Maggie'll take that snuff to the grave with her,' the neighbours would say.

We always joked that turf smoke was her only perfume for we were aware of it as soon as she visited us. Years of rough working with the turf and from domestic chores had left their mark; ingrained snuff on her gnarled hands and discoloured finger-nails told of her austere lifestyle.

We heard she had been a pretty girl but her ragged hair and lined face were now her trademark look. It was obvious she no longer spent much time on personal care. Like many another girl she had been a devoted daughter to her parents, totally self-

133

sacrificing for years until they died, both in their nineties, leaving Maggie alone in her little cottage and with only her fund of stories for company.

Maggie was no recluse, however, and many was the hour she would spend in neighbouring houses yarning till late into the evening. All in the district knew old Maggie and they enjoyed her visits as much as she herself. She was a great source of news for them. Her blackened stumps of teeth were testimony to years of poor diet and self-neglect.

But she had eyes only for Mick Donegan in spite of several suitors who came calling to her door. She had long had a strong notion of Mick who had been a bit of a wanderer in his youth, although he hadn't left that townsland in Inishowen ever since he had inherited his uncle's shop at the other end of the parish. It was a modest business and it was said that Mick had also come into some of his uncle's money, a man known to have left behind a few pounds. Maggie and other girls in the area were all vying for Mick's attention, but he showed no interest in any of them.

The shop became his only concern after he'd returned home and he gave it his full attention, for romance did not interest Mick at all. So Maggie remained single and as time passed she grew old in her home place, spending her nights visiting neighbours, endlessly chatting and enjoying her snuff. And she still spoke often of Mick although now people had became aware of a certain sourness in her tone as she did so.

We children looked on in amazement as Maggie dipped her fingertips into her snuff box before loudly sniffing it up her nose, then rubbing her hands together and continuing with her story. She'd talk at length of Mick's reputed wealth and of how none of it ever saw the 'light o' day. An' who'll git it when he goes?' she'd scowl, 'for he has neither chick nor child. Sure he wouldn't give wan o' them weans (children) there a sweetie.'

We children picked up on her dislike for the man as she spoke. 'Aye, he's a tight one I can tell yez,' was always her parting shot, as she inhaled another refill of snuff with a defiant flourish. As she grew older her bitterness became more evident and we were aware of her change from erstwhile, agreeable storyteller. When she spoke of 'that Mick Donegan,' there was always an edge to her tone, forever begrudging him his money.

However, like Maggie herself, Mick was getting no younger and he had to sell his little shop for which by all accounts he'd received a 'good penny'.

'He must have a million by this time,' scowled Maggie to someone.

Meanwhile, Mick passed his days alone and sometimes did a morning's fishing. As it turned out to be a severe winter his fishing activity came to a halt and he remained indoors until round about Christmas. He was reported ill and Fr. O'Donnell at Mass one cold morning in January asked for prayers for Mick's soul. 'He was a good charitable man.' Maggie raised her eyebrows and some mutterings were exchanged at this. 'He has appointed me to look after his affairs', continued Fr. O'Donnell 'and he has left nothing.' There was a gasp from his congregation, but then he concluded, 'I have receipts and thanksgivings from missionaries and charitable organisations the world over. Mick's charity knew no bounds.'

Brian Donaghy is a retired primary school teacher and is married to Catherine. They have two adult children, one of whom is married. She has two little daughters who delight their grandparents with their company. He very much enjoys reading and writing. He has had quite a few stories published in Ireland's Own *and he has previously also appeared in the* Ireland's Own Anthology.

You've Only Got One Life

By Joan Treacy,
Leixlip, Co. Kildare

*Teacher Stephen is approaching his 50th birthday and is feeling
like his life is stuck in a rut. He felt he had to do something
different and so ended up in in a trendy bar on the way home
from work, the sort of place he would usually studiously avoid.
He was not comfortable and things did not improve when he
met a former student …*

S TEPHEN DIDN'T KNOW what had possessed him. He
should have been going in his front door right now to be
greeted by the comforting smell of a home-cooked dinner.
It was the sort of place he usually avoided – pretentiously decorated with big chandeliers that looked like they came from a medieval
banquet hall, wall-to-wall wooden panelling and furnishings that
seemed to have been taken from the inside of a church.

It was a place for the young and the fashionable – and he felt he
stuck out like a sore thumb in his functional slacks and pullover,
sitting in the wooden pew in front of his pint, while groups of
beautiful people around him sipped cocktails and shorts in round
ice filled glasses.

After leaving work that day, he had decided he was going to
break with his daily routine – a walk in the park and then on home
for dinner. His 50th birthday was approaching and he'd had this
feeling more and more lately of being stuck in a rut. What was it
that people were always saying? 'You've only got one life,' and at
the moment Stephen wasn't convinced he was living his to the

full. Other people seemed to rush around from one activity to the next, whereas Stephen plodded along, the occasional night out with his wife and the monthly pub quiz in his local being his only social outlets.

If he was to try another activity, he liked to know it was happening at least a month before it took place. But lately, with niggling self-doubt creeping in, he was starting to feel that he was missing out on life and to worry that he might be filled with regret on reaching his twilight years. So here he was. It may not have been much but at least he had acted spontaneously coming here tonight.

'Anybody sitting here?'

A young man with a long and bushy beard wearing a formal waistcoat over his jeans, gestured at the empty seat opposite Stephen. He shook his head, …

'No. It's all yours.'

The drinks were on the table and the youth was sitting opposite him but now a young woman appeared, wearing ripped jeans and black lipstick, and she was looking directly at Stephen.

'Oh my God! Crawley! Oops sorry. Mr. Frawley!'

He gave her a watery smile. He had been feeling uncomfortable as it was, without one of his ex-pupils turning up.

'Oh hello, eh.' He tried desperately to recall her name.

'Kathy O'Reilly. You taught me history for the Leaving Cert in 2016. Do you not remember?'

'Of course,' said Stephen.

'How are you getting on? Did you go on to study the subject any further?'

Kathy had her arms folded.

'Fat chance of that,' she said.

'It can be useful all the same,' said Stephen. 'They recommend that you have a good knowledge of history if you're interested in becoming a journalist, for instance.'

Kathy leaned across the table.

'What I mean is, I got such a low mark that I wasn't even offered a place in university. If I hadn't failed history I'm sure I would have got on to the arts course.'

'That's a pity,' said Stephen, 'but maybe you didn't put the work in. I don't remember you taking a big interest in class.'

'No one ever took an interest in your class,' Kathy's voice had developed into a snarl.

'You moved through the material far too slowly. We complained several times to the head but nothing was done about it. Well, I want to let you know that you messed up my life by being a rubbish teacher and I'm not the only one. Adele Boylan didn't get enough points for college either and now she is actually stacking shelves, thanks to you.'

'But, you can't blame …'

'I've always thought it a real shame that incompetent teachers can't be sacked in Ireland,' her bearded companion butted in.

'The way it stands, it's not a level playing field for pupils sitting exams. The ones who haven't been prepared properly are at a disadvantage through no fault of their own.'

Kathy stood up.

'Come on, Jack. Let's go and sit somewhere else.'

Jack stood up.

'Grab the drinks, will you? There's a seat over there near the bar. Come on, hurry up.' Kathy was across the room in a flash. Jack picked the drinks up, spilling a bit of his beer as he did so, and scuttled after her.

Stephen was left alone staring into his pint with a heavy heart. He'd been feeling bad enough about himself lately without being subjected to this blistering attack. It had hurt to be told he was a rubbish teacher. He tried so hard to instil a love of history into his pupils. He felt it was important for them to understand how past events can shape the future but clearly this wasn't what constituted good teaching. From what both Jack and Kathy were saying, he should be more mindful of the fact that his pupils were only there to cram for exams.

Forget fully understanding the subject matter, it was more important to ensure they were able to reel off everything they'd learned by rote. But Stephen's style was more slow and deliberate. He didn't like to rush through the course. Maybe he had become a dinosaur in a world where the points you get in your Leaving Cert were the only indication of a proper education.

And when he thought about it, this tendency to move slowly applied to all aspects of his life, not just his teaching methods. He had lived in the same house, been married to the same wife and worked in the same school for thirty years now. There was no doubt about it, he was a dull and uninteresting person. He needed to break out and become more adventurous but it was hard to change the habits of a lifetime.

He thought of his work colleague who had gone deep sea diving in the Galapagos this year. His lyrical tales of swimming with brightly coloured marine life in the depths of the ocean, had made Stephen's yearly trip to the same Spanish resort seem dull by comparison. The only sea life he ever encountered in the water there were jellyfish. Maybe it was time he tried something different – a trek across the Himalayas perhaps, or even a cycling holiday in France. The truth was, though, that Stephen couldn't imagine himself doing either.

He glanced over at Kathy, who was sitting at the bar, holding her mobile phone in one hand and lifting peanuts from a dish, casually throwing them into her mouth, with the other. You had to admire her dexterity. Multi-tasking was a skill that he had never mastered.

His pint glass was empty and a big part of him wanted to go home but something propelled him up to the bar to get another one. Maybe it was the voice in his head that had now taken hold and was continuously telling him to do something about this rut he was in.

There were a lot of people waiting to be served and Stephen stood behind them thinking that there should be more than one person serving in such a busy city centre pub. Five minutes later, he was still there and he felt a nudge from behind.

'Will ye wave at him, for God's sake? You'll never get served just standing there.'

'Sorry, you're right,' Stephen said.

He never had been one for pushing himself forward. Maybe that was why he had got left behind in life, still in the starting block while everyone else was sprinting around the track.

Kathy had become more animated and was waving her arms around as she spoke into the phone. Then she broke into loud hiccupy laughter that could be heard over the hum of chatter in the bar. It must be great to be so unselfconscious, to have no fear of drawing attention to yourself, thought Stephen gloomily, as he lifted his pint glass up for another sip.

It was then that he heard another noise. It reminded him of the choking rasping sound his cat always made before he was about to get sick. He looked up and he saw Kathy had got down from her stool and was bent over, clearly trying to dislodge something from her throat. Jack was beside her, banging her back but it didn't seem to be making any difference. You could hear her whooping for breath now and her face was starting to turn blue.

'Somebody do something,' Jack's voice was near hysterical, but nobody seemed to be able to help. They just watched with shocked faces.

Stephen got up from his stool and made his way over.

'Take it easy. 'You're banging her back too fast,' he said.

'Come on. Let me try to help out.'

He took hold of her and performed the Heimlich manoeuvre, putting his arms around her waist and sharply thrusting her stomach, the way he'd been taught on the six month first aid course he'd done the previous year. The headmaster had insisted at least one member of staff attend and Stephen had found himself being nominated.

The peanut that was lodged in Kathy's throat came flying out, landing with a plop in someone's cocktail on a table opposite the bar. Kathy's face slowly came back to normal as she took in gulps of air.

'Shouldn't eat those peanuts so fast,' said Stephen. 'I'd take my time with them in future. And it might be an idea to try not to cram so many in at once.'

'Thanks Sir.' There were tears of fright running down her face.

'Yeah, thanks eh, Mr. Frawley,' Jack said.

Stephen got his jacket and took his leave of the bar. Suddenly he felt hungry and he wondered if his wife had kept some chicken curry for him. He was feeling a lot better about himself now. After all, if he hadn't been too slow to come up with an excuse to avoid that first aid course, it could well have been curtains for Kathy tonight. Maybe it wasn't so bad to plod along after all. It was true you only have one life, but he had just learnt that sometimes being in a hurry and feeling you have to do everything at once, can end it prematurely.

Joan Treacy is a stay-at home-mum to two boys. She has been writing for about five years and has produced one novel, a comedy called Pursued *which she self-published on Amazon where it was well received. She has also written numerous short stories and two were published in* Ireland's Own. *She was also shortlisted for Dalkey Festival's Creative Writing competition in 2017 in the short story category. Her main genres are drama and comedy.*

For the One I Loved Best

BY FIDELMA MAHON,
EDENDERRY, CO. OFFALY

*Remembering growing up with a much-loved grandmother and
her traditional way of life. During the summer months the
back door would always be open, her apron clad form sitting
on an old brown kitchen chair thumbing her rosary and looking
out at the little birds that lighted on her line, picking at
the crumbs she had thrown out to them …*

OUR TWO BACK gardens were connected by a well-worn pathway and a gap through the hedge. I was five years old when I began sleeping with my newly widowed grandmother at night. I would toddle up the garden path each evening, calling back to my mother's shape standing guard at the back door, 'Goodnight Ma, goodnight.' I was reassured when I heard her voice ring out: 'Goodnight, goodnight.'

The garden light only reached so far along the way and then I was in complete darkness. The huge oak trees in the rector's field beside us would churn about on windy nights throwing spectral shapes of empty branches like long bony fingers searching in the moonlight. 'It's only the sea, the sea, the beautiful sound of the sea,' I would tell myself. This is what I imagined the sea would sound like. I had never seen the sea but I knew that one day I would.

Grandmother had a small beige coloured Stanley range which rarely went out except to clean it, that was Saturday's dirty job. During the summer months the back door would always be open, her apron-clad form sitting on an old brown kitchen chair thumbing her rosary and looking out at the little birds that lighted on her line, picking at the crumbs she had thrown out to them, or the little white butterflies that landed on the cabbage plants.

The kettle was always full and just boiling off the hob. She'd pull it across and we'd have sweet tea and her own freshly baked brown bread. She would swing open the oven door in winter and resting her leg on my lap I would tell her all my stories from school. She had an innate love of stories, poetry and song. I learned all the old songs and poems from listening to her.

We sang songs long into the night, two souls in a house empty of kith and kin – our breath throwing out funnels of fog on cold winter nights. In summer time we slept downstairs, wrapped up in flour bag sheets she had sewn together. If I had been taught a new prayer, poem or song in school, she would make me write it out for her so we could recite it or sing it together.

She and my grandfather Joe reared six children, with no fridge and no washing machine, and cooking on the range. She showed me the welts on her hands, still bubbling beneath her paper-thin skin from wringing out clothes. I collected water from the well for her in a red bucket and we ate and drank everything fresh and home-made.

The milk bottle delivered to the door stood in a ceramic bucket of cold water covered by a tea towel and the butter was kept in a dish in the cupboard. She baked every day, fresh brown bread, white bread, griddle bread or currant bread. The memory still lingers of the taste of country butter and jam, or a slice of boiled ham and cheese, with tea out of her scalded teapot poured into her best china cups.

I would leave for school after eating breakfast in my own house, counting the hours until I'd be home again. I was allowed sleep in 'til half nine on Saturdays. Every second Saturday I had to go to Confession. Some Saturdays the local lads about would leave a rabbit or two hanging from the door knob and after cleaning out the range she would skin and clean them and soon the most delicious rabbit stew would be bubbling on the range.

Afternoons were for the cleaning ritual, cleanliness being next to godliness. She would draw the curtains, fill a basin with hot water in front of the range and strip for a top to toe clean. I had to face the Sacred Heart picture while she washed, my head almost touched the lamp. I was allowed to turn around and wash her completely when I turned fourteen and my head was over the lamp.

If she needed anything she used to stick a tea towel in the window, my mother would drop everything and run up the path in case there was something up. Once she tripped over the fender, fell and broke her wrist. On Sunday after Mass she would fry rashers and field mushrooms in salted butter and the tea towel in the window meant the fry was ready. Ma and I would arrive for our breakfasts, our mouths watering, three women talking over the week's events – who died, who gave birth, who got married or the price of tea.

My first night in Nambour, Queensland, Australia; and the screeching sound of kookaburras, dark corners where huge spiders hid, cicada's buzzing in the hot humid air and I with a huge double bed all to myself. I was nineteen years old, it was my first time to sleep alone and my first time away. I cried all night for the one I loved best and hummed myself to sleep.

Fidelma Mahon is from Edenderry, County Offaly. She lived in Australia for a number of years in her twenties. She came home and married Tony Coady, goldsmith and artist, and they had their own business for a number of years. She returned to college at age forty and studied for a BA in English and History and completed a Master's in Irish Literature and Cultural Studies at Maynooth University. She enjoys reading and writing and gives regular talks on various writers in Offaly libraries. She is a regular contributor to Sunday Miscellany *on RTE Radio. 'My beautiful grandmother loved* Ireland's Own *and she'd be so proud to be remembered with this published piece.'*

'No Enemy but Time'

By Clare McAfee,
Ballycastle, Co. Antrim

James and Sarah are coming towards the end of their lives after being together for fifty happy years, and they constantly reflect on their times together, the good and the difficult. The bed of roses they had anticipated all those years ago had not been without its fair share of thorns …

MOST PEOPLE CALLED her Sally or Mrs McGreevy, but to her husband James she was always Sarah. He had heard that it meant 'princess' or 'queen' and thought the more formal version suited her better. Besides, it was after all her baptismal name. They were waiting for their son Anthony's phone call in the sitting-room, which had been converted into their bedroom due to Sarah's increasing immobility as the bathroom was downstairs.

Sarah sat in bed propped up with white pillows, gazing without interest at the television with the sound turned to mute. Although the phone was on a small table beside her she did not want to risk missing it ringing. These were the days before mobile phones, otherwise she certainly would have owned one. In the silence the steady ticking of the clock on the mantelpiece was audible.

Sarah was like an ivory coloured rose which had begun to fade but anyone could see that she had once been a great beauty. To James she was still completely beautiful. Even after fifty years he could hardly believe he'd had the good fortune to persuade this lovely woman to marry him. He remembered how she had been when they first met; a laughing, vivacious girl who loved to dress up and go to dances. She could have had her pick of any of the men there but for some reason she was attracted to him.

It pained James for her sake to think that she could now barely walk, even with crutches, she who could once perform all the dance steps so well. However, she hadn't lost her sense of humour. If they were out and someone produced a camera she would throw the crutches away from her and use her husband's arm for support, giving the impression that she was perfectly well. 'Just auld stinking pride' she would whisper with a conspiratorial wink of her eye.

James let his mind slide back over the decades. Sarah had wanted to go to see the North West 200, the motorbike road races at Armoy, and James had borrowed a car from a workmate to take her there. It was then he had hatched his daring plan and during a lull in the roar of the motor bikes and the shouts of the spectators, he had boldly asked Sarah to marry him.

Even now, thinking back, he could hardly believe his luck. Everything had seemed to happen in slow-motion … her look of surprise, the sparkle of realisation in her eyes, the smile forming on her lips as she voiced her consent and the welcome feel of her loving arms embracing him. James had felt like the King of the World. Later, during the drive back home to Ballymoney, he had reflected on the idea of how awkward that journey would have been if she had rejected his proposal.

'Is that clock right, James?' Sarah enquired looking towards the clock on the mantelpiece.

'I think so,' he replied.

'Anthony's late this evening,' she observed anxiously, 'I hope there's nothing wrong,'

James checked his watch. 'Well I think that clock is a little bit fast. I'm sure he'll phone soon.'

'I'm sure you're right.'

James glanced out the window at Sarah's flower-garden. The season was ending. They were lucky to have this pretty house in Margaret Avenue. When they first married they had lived for a few years in a respectable terraced house in Charlotte Street which James had always felt uneasy about.

Initially, he had attributed what he felt to his imagination. Sometimes he would hear footsteps on the stairs at night when they were all in bed and on occasion their bedroom door would burst open as they slept. He would wake up when this happened trying to convince himself that the phenomenon was caused by a draught. However, once he had placed a large chest against the door to keep it shut and he had awakened that night to see the door being pushed open eerily slowly. He had forced himself to rise and investigate but had found no intruder.

From then on, he had been certain there was a ghostly presence in the house. He had not mentioned his suspicions to Sarah for fear of frightening her, little realising that she too had misgivings for she had often felt that an unseen person was watching her.

The truth of the matter came to light when Sarah had asked her younger sister Jean to babysit for them while she and James had a rare outing to a supper dance. They had returned to find the house empty and a note saying Jean had decamped with the children to her mother's residence in Townhead Street.

When they had met up with her she had explained, 'I knew I was too long there when I saw auld Mrs Shields coming down the stairs.' Mrs Shields was the previous occupant who had died in the house. The search for new accommodation had been started the very next day.

Sarah gazed at her husband with concern noting that he looked tired. Well, he was an old man now. They were both old. What a ridiculous idea that was when inside she still felt she was eighteen. She wondered if James felt like that too. Their marriage was a solid one but the bed of roses she'd hoped for had not been without its thorns.

They had been blessed with three children, a boy and two girls, all difficult births but worth the pain. She loved her family dearly. A frown crossed her face as she recalled the fateful day years ago when James had almost been taken from her. He had been working in the building trade as a plasterer for a local firm. Every morning the works van picked him up and took him to the current building site.

On one tragic day James was sitting in the passenger seat beside the driver. As they travelled along one of the other workmen had spoken from the back of the van. 'Jimmy' he said, 'would you mind swapping seats with me? I'm feeling a bit sick and sitting up front might help me.'

'I don't mind where I sit,' James had responded so the driver stopped the vehicle and the two men exchanged seats. They had set off again, but they had not travelled very far when there was an almighty bang as the van collided with another vehicle, a lorry as James later discovered. He had been knocked unconscious by the crash.

Sarah well remembered the distressing news being brought to her at her home.

'There's been an accident, Mrs. McGreevy,' the foreman had said when she answered his knock at the door. She had almost stopped breathing with the shock.

'Is James dead?' she had whispered fearfully.

'He'll survive,' the man had assured her. 'He's in hospital, I'll drive you there now if you want to see him.' On the way he had told her of the twist of fate which had saved her husband's life.

'It could have been so much worse Mrs. McGreevy. James had been sitting in the front seat, but a workmate asked to change places with him and the man who took James' place was killed outright in the crash.'

Sarah had pitied the wife of the dead man, but it was impossible not to be glad that James had been spared.

It had taken several operations to restore James to health and he received financial compensation for his injuries. With this they bought a little Morris Minor car to give them some independence and a piano so that their children could have the opportunity their parents never had to learn to play music.

The children were all grown up now and living in their own homes, the car had been replaced a few times, but the piano was still there, seldom used now except as a setting to display the grandchildren's framed photographs.

Sarah's eyelids grew heavy and soon she slumped back against the supporting pillows and began to doze. The dream she had was a recurring one. She was walking in High Street with quite a crowd of people going to the shops. Suddenly everyone started to panic as a rumour spread about a bomb being planted in one of the shops. Sarah's immediate concern was for her daughter, Bernadette, who worked in the teashop of The Brown Jug bakery.

She began to run towards the café but oh, how slowly one runs in dreams. Fear welled up in her as she tripped on the pavement. The ground seemed to rush up to meet her, but her eyes snapped open just before the impact.

Sadly, the dream was an enactment of a real incident which had happened in Ballymoney during the Northern Irish Troubles. It turned out that the 'bomb' had been a hoax, but Sarah had been injured by the fall. In fact, that was the start of the problems with her legs, for despite medical treatment, arthritis had set in over the years causing her much pain and affecting her agility.

Nevertheless, she often said, 'I don't regret what happened. If I had my life to live over again then I would always try to save my children.'

The telephone rang and of course it was Anthony phoning from England, as he did every Sunday evening.

'Hello Mum.'

'Hello son, how are things with you?'

She was animated now, keeping her voice light so he would not know she was in pain. It was harder to hide things like that from her daughters Bernadette and Jennifer who lived nearby, but Anthony's family had moved to Buckinghamshire and she did not want them worrying about her so far away.

'Geraldine says to thank you for her birthday card and the money you enclosed. Mum you should be keeping your money to spend on you and Dad.'

'Oh, son it wasn't much! And of course, I wanted to spoil my granddaughter a little bit.'

'Well it was a lovely card Mum. You always choose one with a nice verse inside.'

'Yes, well I was never very fond of school, but I did like poetry.'

'I remember you used to recite one to us about *"The Old Woman of the Roads"*. That was a great poem.'

'That's by Padraic Colum and it's one of my favourites. Well, your Dad's anxious to get speaking to you so I'll pass you over to him. Goodnight son!'

'Goodnight Mum.'

When the phone call was over they sat in silence for a few minutes. The clock ticked on steadily eroding their future.

Eventually James spoke. 'I heard you saying to Anthony about the poetry. You have a good memory for that kind of thing.'

'Sure, they drilled everything into us in our schooldays,' she laughed, 'but funnily enough they didn't kill my love for poetry.'

'Your sister, Jean, God rest her, was good at reciting that long poem *"The Wreck of the Hesperus"*.'

'Oh yes, Jean was a far better scholar than me. She memorised many poems. She knew every word of *"The Burial of Sir John Moore"*… and she died aged just sixty-nine. I do miss her.'

'*"The Burial of Sir John Moore"* how does that go?'

'I only remember bits of it. I know the last four lines:

> '*Slowly and sadly we laid him down*
> *From the field of his fame fresh and gory;*
> *We carved not a line, and we raised not a stone*
> *But left him alone with his glory.*'

'Who wrote that?'

'I think it was an Irishman, Charles Wolfe.'

'It's a fine piece of writing but it's a bit depressing Sarah.'

'You're right as always, James. Let's have a cup of tea and a biscuit to cheer ourselves up and maybe you could check the paper to see if there's anything worth watching on television.'

And so, they avoided the topic which was always on the back of both their minds these days … which of them would die first? They had faced so many problems together, but the worst would be the inevitable parting death would bring. Both firmly believed in a heavenly life hereafter but neither wanted to leave the other to soldier on in this world without them. As the poet William Butler Yeats said:

> '*The innocent and the beautiful*
> *Have no enemy but time.*'

Clare McAfee was born on the night of the Blue Moon, September 26, 1950 – atmospheric conditions made the lunar orb appear blue that night, it was reported. She started work as a primary school teacher in September 1973 in Derry city and although it was the time of The Troubles she stayed there for 13 years. After that she got a teaching post in her hometown of Ballycastle where she worked until retirement last year after 33 years. For a hobby she loves to write stories and poetry and she has had quite a few items published in Ireland's Own *over the years. This is her fourth appearance in the* Ireland's Own Anthology.

151

King of the Hills

By Pauline O'Dwyer-Grady,
Killarney, Co. Kerry

*Billy, a defiant problematic and menacing figure, took possession of
the road and those who were walking were vulnerable depending on
his mood. He stood his ground and stared when challenged. He had
prominent horizontal eyes, a long matted beard, small ears standing
erect on his head and an obnoxious smell …*

HE PATROLLED 'THE TURRETS' up and down for
days. He stuck his head in curiosity here and there in
doorways, gateways and avenues. He trampled lawns
and flower beds, pulling and nibbling at whatever vegetation took
his fancy. On the road, traffic, though scarce, had to slow down
almost to a stop to avoid a collision and he was a menace to
anyone on a bicycle.

He took possession of the road. He was a defiant problematic
and menacing figure, and those who were walking were vulnerable
depending on his mood. He stood his ground and stared when
challenged. He had prominent horizontal eyes, a long matted
beard, small ears which stood erect on his head and a foul
obnoxious smell.

His long coarse thick wool coat of varied mixtures of grey and
black draped over his deep shaped body and short, strong-hooved
legs. Great impressive, long curved horns bejewelled his head. No
one knew where he came from, the King of the hills, Billy a wild
buck goat.

Tom our neighbour, a small stocky man, wore thick round glasses and used a walking stick. It was his daily routine to go to the house his son occupied to do a little kitchen gardening. Billy followed Tom and stuck his head over the half-door when Tom went into the kitchen. Tom, annoyed, thought he could frighten Billy away by waving his walking stick, clapping his hands and shouting 'Go away,' but the little bit of drama only increased Billy's excitement all the more.

Grabbing the sweeping brush from the kitchen, Tom went outside swinging and waving the brush to scare off Billy, but taking up the challenge Billy had other ideas. Shaking his head, lowering his horns, feet scratching off the rough cobbled path across from the house, he got ready to charge. Tom, recognising the stance, knew he had to take cover and ran back into the house, Billy hot on his heels.

Billy began a session of head-butting the half- door. It is difficult to pinpoint exactly how long the head-butting lasted, but I was rooted to the ground in fright. I had visions of Billy breaking down the half door and knew Tom was no match for Billy's anger or gusto.

Eventually help came and the goat was driven into the nearby field where he had the company of a cow. It was my job to drive the cow to the yard to be milked every evening. I kept a close watch on Billy but he never bothered me. He stayed under the crab tree at the other side of the field. It was late August or early September; there was a good crop of crab apples and a long ditch of varied vegetation that kept him happy.

Goats, I discovered, are in season from August to December and it is actually called 'the rut.' The long horned King of the Hills was sometimes known as the poor man's cow and was kept for its meat, hair, and hides.

Goat's milk products are now renowned for their health benefits and it is considered to be much more digestible than cow's milk.

With the increasing demand and consumption of goat's milk, mild cheese, yoghurt, and ice cream, goat farming has expanded. Creams and soaps made from goat's milk are extremely effective in the treatment of eczema.

The bodhrán (bowraan) is a traditional, single headed basic drum, predominantly played with a tipper or beater. The head is traditionally covered in goatskin, though calfskin, deerskin and plastic are now common materials. As well as the skin, the bones from the carcase of the goat are also cured and when dried and hardened can create a new charm.

Methods of building and playing the bodhrán are varied and when the dried dead bones are clacked on dried dead skin by the fingers of the expert tipper, music of the dead becomes alive.

In ancient pre-Christian celebrations, the Puck or Buck or He goat was a symbol of fertility. Ancient superstitions also regarded the goat with caution; it was believed that the Devil could appear as a goat with horns and cloven hooves.

Billy grazed peacefully for several weeks in the field but the fear of him getting free still lingered. Eventually arrangements were made with the owner of a cattle truck and Billy's passage was booked. I never heard exactly where Billy went but that was the last we saw of him.

Pauline O'Dwyer-Grady lives in Killarney, Co. Kerry, with her husband James, but both are natives of An Ráth, Co Cork. They have two children and three grandchildren. A full time housewife when the children were growing up, Pauline was interested in reading, music, gardening, cooking, knitting, sewing and crochet. They moved to Killarney in 1982 and she joined the local Concert Band, playing alto saxophone in many competitions with them around Ireland and abroad. She is researching the family history and genealogy and writing the stories of her ancestors lives from the Famine, Boer War, War of Independence and Civil War. This is her first entry in the Ireland's Own Anthology.

Should Ambition be Made of Sterner Stuff?

By Tony McGettigan,
Dundrum, Dublin

Despite her protestations that she is very happy as things are, and that she keeps herself busy, John decides that Nora, his wife of forty years, needs to get out more, take up something new that she always wanted to do. A chance to do just that arrives unexpectedly, but John's reaction catches her by surprise …

IT BEGAN PLEASANTLY over a cup of tea by the fireside. No one could have imagined how it would end. John took Nora's small hand in his big work-roughened one and said, 'It's hard to believe that we'll be married forty years next Friday. Four children reared and flown and here we are on our own again like we started.'

Nora smiled at him as she had been doing for forty years, and more. John continued, with sudden energy. 'Do ye know what I've been thinking? I've been thinking you must be finding the days very long, here on yer own when I'm at work. It'd be good for ye to get out and take up somethin' new, somethin' you've always wanted to do.'

He paused as if he expected Nora to jump in with an immediate list of pent-up desires, but she didn't, so he continued. 'Things ye've never had time for 'cause ye were always lookin' after us.'

'Oh, I am happy as I am,' Nora replied softly. 'Between meals and housework, and reading, and my music and charity work, and, of course, my friends and the family, my days go by happily.'

'Naw, housework an' readin' an' gossipin', it'd drive ye outa yer skull. Ye'd be better off gettin' outa the house an' takin' up somethin' challenging. I saw it on the TV, "The Retirement Revolution". It explained everythin'.'

'But I do get out of the house. I have good friends, thank God, and I love my music and my reading and the Charity Shop work.'

'I'm only just sayin' like, I hate to think of ye here by yerself all the day.'

'But I am not here by myself all day! I do go out to my music studies and the Book Club and the Charity Shop, and I socialise with my friends, and the children call whenever they can. Honestly John, don't worry about me. I am perfectly happy as I am, but I'll look around for something new if it will make you happy.'

'Ye know it would. Yer young yet an' ye should be developin' yerself, like it said on the TV, cultivatin' yer undeveloped talents, not goin' to seed doin' nothin'. That's a big danger ye know as ye get older, goin' ta seed, that's what they said on the TV.'

Nora smiled.

Shortly after that, Nora and her best friend Kitty were chatting in Clinking Cups Café.

'Wait'll I tell ye, Nora, ye'll never guess what I'm doin' tamorra.'

'No, probably not; something exciting?'

'How'd ye guess, very excitin'. It might come to nothin' but it'll be fun anyway.'

'Well … tell me … what is it?'

'Somethin' I never thought I'd get into.'

'Sky-diving … rock-climbing … marathon running?'

'Nooo … I'm off for an audition … for a part on TV!'

'What? For a part on TV?' Nora was surprised.

'Yeh! I saw it in the paper, ye know, the free one they push in the door. A headline in it caught me eye, "Could This Be Your Opportunity to Star on TV?"'

'Could this be your opportunity to star on TV?'

'Yeh! An' it could; that's what's excitin'.'

'Gosh!' was all Nora could say.

'You can come too, if yer interested.'

'Me! What's it about?'

'Auditions for a TV programme! They're bein' held tamorra in the hall in Dunleary. They're looking for ladies in their fifties, with attractive, white hair'.

'But I'm sixty-one!'

'Ye don't have to be what they say, it's only TV! And anyway, you'd easily pass for fifty. I might be in trouble though.'

'No you won't!'

'Anyway, are ye interested?'

'But I know nothing about acting and I couldn't act if my life depended on it.'

'Ye don't have to be able to act I'm tellin' ye; it's for TV! And the gas thing is ye get paid for it, hundreds a day if you're selected an' more if you have to speak, even one word.'

'What?'

'Yeh, yeh, hundreds and more if ye open yer mouth at all!'

Nora thought about it.

'I think I'll go. John has been on to me, trying to persuade me to take on a new challenge. Thanks a lot for telling me. It'll be a pleasant surprise for John. I'll go.'

And she did. She was that kind of woman. When she decided on something, then her focus was unwavering, her determination inexhaustible. And she could easily pass for fifty, no bother, and an attractive fifty!

The audition was quite a surprise. Nora noticed quickly, simply by watching what was going on, that Kitty was right, 'ye' did not have to be able to act. All 'ye' had to do was look the part.

If a no-good tough was being cast, anyone with a rough, bony face, the more rugged the better, was a shoo-in. If they were looking for a hard-done-by homeless person, they got a hard-done-by homeless person off the street! So, Nora with her good looks and her silver hair was absolutely made for any attractive-older-woman part.

Nora was cast and so was Kitty. They did not have any lines but were in several scenes. Nora loved it. Kitty loved it. It was great craic. For three weeks they met almost every morning in Clinking Cups Café and went together to that day's location, which was usually in the Dún Laoghaire area, but on two occasions they were taken by taxi to a studio for on-set filming. It was exciting and interesting and everyone they met was pleasant and helpful.

Nora discovered that the camera 'loved her'. The cameraman, who was a woman, the director and the producer told her so. She was not quite sure what it meant but it definitely seemed to be 'a good thing'. It led to her being approached by a lady who was an 'Agent', which Nora thought, and Kitty confirmed, was someone who would make it her job, for a small fee, to acquire other parts for Nora.

Indeed, as this first adventure in the screen trade was drawing to a close, the Agent informed Nora that she had another audition lined up for her in a week's time. Nora was thrilled and Kitty was thrilled for Nora. Kitty had not been approached by an Agent. It looked like her career in TV was destined to be short. Apparently, even in your sixties, good looks take precedence.

At this point Nora felt that she should inform John about the wonderful progress she was making in avoiding 'goin' ta seed doin' nothing'. She had left John under the impression, not that he had made any enquiries, that her time with Kitty was being spent doing charity work or 'gossipin' in Clinking Cups Café.

So, one evening when she and John were enjoying a cuppa in front of the fire, she disclosed all. John's response was totally unexpected. He blew up in anger!

'So that's what ye have been up to an' me thinkin' ye were at yer usual gossipin' an' all the time ye were foolin' me, keepin' me in the dark an' foolin' me up to me eyes! Ye must have had a right laugh at me the pair of ye.'

'No John!' Nora was shocked and upset by his vehemence. 'No John, you know I would never laugh at you like that. I thought you would be pleased. That's why I went. You were at me to get out of the house, to do something new.'

'Somethin' like developin' yerself, like it said on the TV, developin' yer full potential, not somethin' like carryin' on and actin' the eejit in front of strangers.'

'I was not carryin' on, acting the eejit. I was simply being filmed for TV.'

'Oh yeh, that'd be right up yer street alright, havin' everyone gawkin' at ye, admirin' ye an' fussin' over ye.'

'John, are you serious?'

Nora could hardly believe what was happening. In over forty years together she and John had never had a row, had never exchanged accusations, about anything!

'Am I serious, course I'm serious, typical of ya, lookin' for attention, wantin' to be the centre of everythin'. I always knew it but never said it like.'

'I was never 'always looking for attention'.'

'Oh yes ye were! Oh yes ye were! On New Year's Eve in John O'Connor's! Remember? Ye were playin' up to everyone, the centre of attention and ye loved it, ignorin' me as if I wasn't there.'

'John O'Connor's? I do not remember but if it ever happened it must have been years ago. We haven't been in O'Connors on New Year's Eve for years and years!'

'An' when Shankill won the Championship! At the celebrations! Ye had everyone fussin' over ye, tellin' ye how great ye were an' everythin', an' ye weren't even at the match! An' I was at every match an' ignored, ignored I was, completely! Oh, ye loved it, ye couldn't get enough of it, always lookin' for attention, always, an' ignorin' me, oh yeh, I didn't matter.'

'When Shankill won the Championship! When was that? A long time ago anyway, if it ever happened! John, please John, don't get so worked up; please, please, don't be upset. I never looked for attention, nor was I ever the centre of attention.'

But there was no appeasing John. He ranted on – Nora always, always needed to have everyone running after her, always, always looked for attention, enjoying every minute of it, ignoring him as if he weren't there.

Nora tried to break the flow, protesting that it was untrue, but it was no good. John flowed on. 'Appearing on TV is just what ye'd be good at, everyone gawkin' at ye an' fussin' over ye, that'd be right up yer street, right up yer alley, no doubt about it. Nora Gilfoyle! Oh, me mother saw it in ye but I wouldn't listen to her. Nora Gilfoyle, the attention seeker, she saw it in ye right enough, an' warned me, but I never saw it, never saw it … until now!'

Nora could not stop him. Even assuring him that she would never ever seek to be the centre of anything that would exclude him did no good. And it hurt her deeply, this terrible insecurity underlying his love, this strange fear that had been buried and had now exploded without warning.

'Ye were never anythin' but an attention-seeking flirt. Oh, the TV would suit ye down to the ground, down to the ground.'

Nora could take no more. Tears she had striven valiantly to hold back welled up in her eyes and she cried silently, her shoulders heaving. John's tirade stopped immediately. He went to her and put an awkward arm around her shoulders and tried to dry her eyes with his grubby handkerchief.

'Oh, I'm sorry Nora, I'm sorry, please don't cry. I dunno what came over me. Please don't cry. I'm very, very sorry. I am.' He was caressing the back of her neck. 'I love you Nora, ye know I do, you're the best, the very best. I dunno what got into me, I'm sorry, I am. Please stop cryin'.'

Nora stopped crying and John started crying, blubbering, repeating continuously, 'I love you Nora, you're the best, you are, I love you, I do.' Nora took his hand, squeezed it affectionately, pressed it to her cheek and smiled at him.

When Nora told her Agent that she would not be attending the planned audition, her Agent was surprised and a bit annoyed, Nora thought.

'But it's a wonderful opportunity,' her Agent exhorted. 'I could guarantee you regular work. You're a born natural. There's good money in it. All you need is ambition.'

'I have ambition,' Nora replied. 'Lots of it but it's focussed on something entirely different – my own happiness!'

And she did have ambition, lots of it. She was that kind of woman. When she decided on something, then her focus was unwavering, her determination inexhaustible.

Tony McGettigan has had five well received hardback books published by Woodpark Publications exploring aspects of County Cork, in conjunction with photographer Francis Twomey. He was also writer and photographer for The Ascent of Mount Elgon, *an account of a real-life personal travel adventure, and a novel,* The Letter, *a love story set in Kerry and Dublin. He has three times won prizes in the* Ireland's Own *Open Short Story Competition. He is a widower living in Dublin and his interests include writing and reading, hill-walking, theatre and music.*

Carnival Delights

By Vincent J. Doherty,
Burford Gardens, London

*Carnival Week was the highlight of our summer in the 1950s. The
Parochial Field became our showground, fairground and playground
but the carnival wasn't just there, it took over the whole town and
painted it with sunshine, come fair weather or foul, as everybody
joyfully set aside their everyday troubles for something different …*

SUMMER WOULD NEVER have been summer in the
1950s without our carnival. They might have had grander
affairs in faraway places but there was only one as far as the
people of Strabane were concerned. Everybody turned out and
hundreds of visitors from miles around flocked to play a part in
it or just enjoy it.

The Parochial Field became our showground, fairground and
playground but the carnival wasn't just there, it took over the
whole town and painted it with sunshine, come fair weather or
foul. Everybody joyfully set aside their everyday troubles for
something different, a week filled with celebration, jubilation and
spectacle, all in a good cause because Barrack Street Boys needed
a new school, or at least a few more classrooms, and the proceeds
of the carnival would go to the School Building Fund.

Carnival invariably began with a noisy, musical, laughing
parade of floats, bands and jokers of all kinds capering through
the streets on a Sunday afternoon. The town turned out en-masse
to view those parades and there was plenty to view.

162

There were silver bands and brass bands, fife and drum bands and once I was part of a class of twelve-year-old tone deaf boys with no musical talents whatsoever parading as 'The Unmusical Crazy Band' making fools of ourselves, scampering along the route dressed in false faces and clowns' outfits, making a hell of a din with washboards, trumpets, tin drums, tambourines, flutes and anything else that came readily to hand.

Every night throughout Carnival Week there was a raucous funfair loud enough to waken the dead for townlands around with different rides and sideshows such as dodgem cars, chairoplanes and roller coasters. I had three successive rides on the chairoplane one night, flying through the air, the carnival field swaying round and round with the music of the steam organ getting louder and louder until at last I stumbled dizzily off and sank to the ground, sick as a dog.

There was all manner of games where hopeful boys could lose or even win money; shillings or even pounds. We watched the man operating the Crown and Anchor stall like hawks for it was rumoured that somebody had won a fortune there once, although nobody could actually put a name to the lucky winner.

At another stall we rolled our pennies down a chute hoping against hope that they would land squarely on a ten or even twelve square and win us as much as a shilling. I won a veritable fortune, nearly half a crown, on a lucky run there once, but then greedily seeking to increase my winnings lost the lot, penny after penny. I went home heartbroken with empty pockets but maybe the wiser about the joys and sorrows of gambling. One other night on the hoopla stall, I hooped a Toby Jug, chipped but nonetheless a prize.

There was a massive marquee in one corner of the field, the like of which we'd never seen before. That was for special events such as a crowded smoky evening of boxing, blood and sawdust. In between one of the fights Rinty Monaghan, who'd once been

Ireland's very own World Champion, got up and sang. There was equal excitement for another evening of all-in wrestling, a live spectacle with sweaty men throwing one another around a ring, cheered and jeered on by a large baying crowd that took the entertainment far more seriously than did the entertainers themselves.

There was five-a-side football on a sloping pitch and bicycle polo, if you can imagine such a thing, with rules made up as the game went along. There was a weight-lifting contest with stronger men than I'd ever seen. I can remember watching a dog show in the field one afternoon with highly-bred, impeccably behaved pampered pooches from all over the country competing disdainfully with local ill-bred mutts that had no sense of propriety or decorum at all.

There was a gymkhana in that field too, although none of us knowing what a gymkhana was, we called it a horse show, with thoroughbred and less bred ponies and horses jumping round after round or coming to grief on the bar as the jumps went higher and higher.

There were concerts at night with our own Clipper Carlton Showband and singers who wanted to be the next Ruby Murray or another Josef Locke, and there were dances for those who could dance the night away till midnight in St. Pat's Hall.

And the Carnival ended with an Irish Day, a Feis with step dancing, traditional music and solemn recitations. I spent many an hour rehearsing such recitations but I never won anything. Did it always rain on that last day or was that just the way we felt as we said 'Goodbye' to the Carnival for another year?

Vincent Doherty is the only writer to have two entries in this year's Ireland's Own Anthology *— he contributed also the prize-winning memoir* The Railway Station *which appears on page 21.*

I Called You Rose

By Bernie Kirwan,
Gorey Hill, Co. Wexford

Even though her legs were shaking she felt a little more confident with each tentative step and she eventually found herself standing before the wooden casket totally alone. Everyone else was gathered around the chief mourners, quietly talking and shaking hands, which created for Roseanne a quiet space in the midst of the crowd, a golden and unexpected opportunity …

IT WAS A DARK, miserable and stormy evening as Roseanne parked her car near the funeral parlour. Once again, she was crippled with uncertainty and overwhelming doubts as to why she was here, why she had made this journey. Something deep inside told her that she needed to see this through to the very end. At the last minute she had decided to come, she just had to. Rushing through the busy evening traffic she barely made it on time. Tom, her husband, wanted to drive but she insisted on going this journey alone.

Taking a deep breath, she locked her car and walked into the funeral parlour. No one really looked at her – after all she was just another face in a crowd. Even though her legs were shaking she felt a little more confident with each tentative step and so she eventually found herself standing before the wooden casket totally alone.

Everyone else was gathered around the chief mourners, quietly talking and shaking hands. People barely glanced at the coffin, seemingly more intent on talking to the living, which created for Roseanne a quiet space in the midst of the crowd, a golden and unexpected opportunity.

As a nurse she was used to death, and she did understand that people often didn't know what to do when confronted with it. In their uncertainty they often did and said the daftest things. Roseanne had witnessed new life coming into the world in her role as a midwife, and she had held the hands of many people as they took their final breath. Beginnings and endings in the circle of life, each and every one, she knew were a privilege to be a part of.

She felt invisible to everyone around her which was exactly how she wanted it to be. That was the plan after all, to slip in quietly, pay her respects and leave. She looked at the face she had never seen in person before but had imagined religiously. 'It wasn't meant to be like this,' she thought to herself, as she drank in every feature, every line of the 70-year-old woman lying in front of her.

Reaching in, she gently touched the cold hands that were entwined with the customary Catholic rosary beads. Breathing deeply, she remained steadfast in her need to see this through to the end. 'She was here to complete the circle,' she thought as she placed a single red rose beside the coffin.

Time stood still, and it seemed in that moment that there was just the two of them, together at last, but not together at all, she thought sadly. Death had come along unexpectedly and robbed her of the meeting that was finally meant to happen. Beginnings and endings, she thought quietly to herself. It seemed apt, as she stood here alone in this quiet space. It was apt that once, a long time ago at the beginning, there was just the two of them and now here they were again, the two of them at the end. 'That's as it is,' she thought to herself, 'we come into this world alone and ultimately we leave it on our own regardless of who is present.'

Contact had been initiated two years earlier mainly through numerous social workers, when Roseanne was 50 years of age. She decided to make the first move, and over a long time and numerous attempts by the social workers to get Margaret to meet she managed to secure a name and address. Remembering back to that first letter and the numerous attempts to put words down on paper, she had eventually decided to say very little. *'Short was best,'* she realised.

> *My name is Roseanne, and I would*
> *like to meet you.*

Weeks passed with no response. Something inside Roseanne persisted, but two further letters were also met with a deafening silence. After a lot of sleepless nights, and chats with her ever-supportive husband, she decided sadly that for now it just wasn't meant to be. She would leave it for a while and try again later. Working as a midwife kept her busy, but watching and helping new life into the world meant Margaret was never too far from her thoughts. No matter how many babies she had helped to deliver, and there had been many, she still saw each and every one as a miracle of life.

Time passed by and arriving in exhausted from work one evening she gathered up the post, flicking through to see if there was anything for her. 'Bills, junk mail and, surprise surprise, more bills,' she thought as she threw them on the table in the hallway. There was one more letter in a pale blue envelope with shaky handwriting addressed to

> *Roseanne Delaney, Orchard Way,*
> *Mullinstown, County Wicklow*

Not recognising the writing, she decided to make herself a cuppa throw off her shoes, put her weary feet up before opening it. Like the envelope, the paper was a pale blue parchment. As she unfolded it she gasped when she saw the address at the top. She had written it often enough, hadn't she?

> *2 Hillview,*
> *Crosstown, Co Cork.*
> *Dear Roseanne.*
> *I am sorry for not writing sooner, but your letter came as such a shock to me. You see, I have never spoken about you to anyone. I'm so sorry Roseanne but I can't meet you, it can never ever be. I'm old now, and life hasn't been easy, too much sadness, too many memories … best left alone … best not spoken about. Dearest Roseanne, please, please forgive me.*
> *By the way, I named you Rose in the few moments I was allowed to hold you all those years ago. You will always be that to me. There's not a day goes by that I don't pray for you and hope that life has been good. I do love your name, Roseanne. I've always loved roses, you see, especially when they are in bloom. They need love and care for that to happen. I hope you have been loved and cared for my dearest Rose.*
> *Signed, Margaret Cullen.*

Roseanne didn't even notice the silent tears falling as she read the words in front of her, the pain of rejection hitting her hard all over again. Yet, somewhere in those words she felt a flicker of love, a connection that was barely noticeable. A connection that was so fragile, but nevertheless, it was something tangible to hold on to, a response, an acknowledgment of sorts.

It was enough for Roseanne to pen another letter, telling Margaret all about her life. She poured fifty-two years of living on to the pages. Once she had started she could not stop. The overwhelming need to nurture this very fragile communication that had been made was more than her life's worth.

And so, began a relationship of sorts, through the power of the written word. A mutual gradual trust seemed to develop through the simplicity of letter writing. Neither made demands on each other but spoke honestly about their lives. Roseanne never asked about meeting again, afraid to threaten the beautiful relationship that was being created.

She knew Margaret felt safe and as a result there was an openness and honesty in their mutual sharing on paper, an openness that may not be as strong if they spoke to each other face to face. Roseanne knew there was something very special happening as letters went back and forth. Putting pen to paper seemed to allow each to tell their story in a non-threatening and safe way that was beautiful in its purity.

The letters became a journal of sorts, a story of two lives filled with love, sadness, happiness and life's experiences. They managed to form a tender and loving bond, a connection that was so precious she would do nothing to jeopardise it. *'For now, maybe even forever, it's enough,'* she thought.

Roseanne learned all about Margaret's life, her two daughters, only a few years younger than herself; her husband, who had passed away, and the ups and downs of her fractious relationship with her older daughter, Ann.

And Margaret too learned all about Roseanne's own life, her husband Tom, her two daughters Deirdre and Helen who had flown the nest in the last year, leaving Tom and herself alone once again. She told her all about her life as a nurse, a job she loved and was proud to do. She shared funny and sad stories with Margaret of people she met along the way.

She shared her own breast cancer experience, her own diagnosis that urged her to live life to the fullest. That urged her to revisit and retrace her past in a compassionate way, leading her to where she was at right now on her journey of discovery. Over the last while something very subtle had started to come into the letters. Margaret had started to gently hint about meeting. Roseanne allowed her to be the one to initiate it, never forcing the issue, just allowing the idea to naturally grow and blossom over time.

The last thing she wanted to do was break this tender connection they had together. Recently Margaret became more direct in her request to meet. *'We will do it soon,'* she said, *'new beginnings, new memories to create,'* were her words in her last letter, a letter filled with love and warmth that poured off the pages. Roseanne was looking forward to the meeting with a peace in her heart. At this stage she felt they knew each other very well, having shared so much in their letters. She looked forward to finally sitting down together and making the circle complete. Her husband, Tom, who had supported her all the way was over the moon and held her tightly as she told him the news of the intended meeting

Enjoying a leisurely cup of coffee in her local hotel two days ago, she was reading *The Irish Independent*. As she always did, she read through the death notices, a habit she had developed from working as a nurse. And there it was.

Margaret Cullen … after a short illness, in the loving care of her daughters Marie and Ann.

Roseanne read it again and again to make sure that she wasn't dreaming, but it was as it said. Margaret had passed away. It was over. Roseanne felt numb as the finality of her passing hit her in waves of disbelief. 'So, that's it' she thought to herself sadly; 'that's the end of the story.'

She sat for a while longer resigning herself to the new reality of her loss, reflecting over the many letters full of love that had passed between them. 'No,' she thought suddenly, 'they were real, behind each word was our life story, I'm real, I do exist, we did exist, I have to go, I have to see her.' She checked and double checked the funeral times and her mind was made up. She had to be there, she had to complete this circle of her life. Beginnings and endings. Together at the beginning and together at the end, life and death.

Roseanne was brought back from her thoughts as a woman gently touched her shoulder. She hadn't realised that the tears were coursing down her face, and her hands were still wrapped around the cold hands of the lady she called Margaret, her mother who had given her up for adoption all those years ago.

Glancing up, she was embarrassed to see that everyone was looking at her. As she turned around to see who had touched her shoulder she found herself looking at her own mirror image. 'How did you know my mother?' the lady asked.

Bernie Kirwan is a wife, mother, nurse, blogger and many other things, in a very busy life and she says she is gradually learning the craft of writing and her selection for the Ireland's Own Anthology *was a great source of encouragement to her.*

Crazy Golf and a Clean Shirt

By Geraldine Hannigan,
Lifford, Co. Donegal

*Our creative Mammy created our very own crazy 'golf course'
in our back garden where we could imagine ourselves being
a Jack Nicklaus or a Tom Watson for a day …*

WHEN I WATCHED Rory McIlroy tee off on the first hole in the Irish Open Golf at Portstewart in 2017, my mind drifted back to a hazy Friday morning in July 1964. My mother, God rest her, had designed our very own crazy golf course at the top of our garden. Mammy was always creating fun games for us and the neighbouring children to take part in during the summer holidays.

Although our 'golf course' had only five holes, it was great fun and we could become a Jack Nicklaus or a Tom Watson for the day. The first hole on our 'golf course' was on top of a man-made hill of clay sods. If we didn't land the ball directly on top, it could have easily rolled back down the hill again and end up at our feet. This would lead to roars of laughter from the younger children who were looking on.

Another hole meandered over Daddy's potato drills. On many occasions if Mammy's clothesline got in the way, her snow-white sheets would stop the golf ball in its flight, leaving the washing peppered with tiny round mucky stains. Thankfully, Mammy never complained and we never explained! Sometimes a ball would get lost in the hedge and we'd endure many nettle stings before it was retrieved. Despite these challenges, we managed to finish the course.

Visitors would often partake in a round of our special golf challenges. On this particular Friday morning our local postman, Aengus, had just finished his shift for the day and he decided to have a go. He parked his bicycle and empty mail bag against our summer seat. As it was a warm, sunny day, he removed his coat and shirt and hung them over the bike.

Making his way to the first tee, a small group of neighbours assembled to watch Aengus try to master the course and become the next Tony Jacklin. In the meantime, my mother, who took great pride in her washing skills, spotted the shirt and decided to give it a quick rinse out. As the day was warm, she spread it over the hedge to dry.

Shortly after he'd finished the game, Aengus returned to his bike only to find that his shirt had disappeared. He called to my mother and asked her if she had seen it. He was hoping that it hadn't been dragged away by our neighbour's friendly pooch.

'Don't worry, Aengus,' my mother smiled. 'I gave it a wee wash and it should be dry by now,' she said, pointing to the hedge. 'If you hold on,' she continued, 'I'll give it a quick iron for you.'

'Good on you Leila. More power to your elbow,' Aengus called out cheerfully.

Later, after Aengus had put on his shirt and jacket, he prepared to leave for home. Before he left, he thanked Mammy. 'Where else but in Donegal, would a postman get a round of golf and his shirt washed and ironed in minutes?' He chuckled. Whistling cheerfully, he waved to the gallery as he cycled off.

Alas, the street is quieter now, the children have grown up and most of them have moved away. Aengus has long retired and is enjoying a more relaxed life-style. Our postmen now drive around in mail vans. People seem to be more in a rush these days and there's certainly no time for an impromptu game of Crazy Golf.

The memory of that sunny Friday morning all those years ago remains etched in my mind. I still smile at the fun we had which ended up with Aengus cycling off, happily sporting his freshly laundered shirt.

Geraldine Hannigan is a native of Lifford, Co Donegal. She has five children and eleven grandchildren. She's a member of the local Gateway Writers' Group. Her hobbies are reading, travelling, swimming and creative writing. Geraldine's work has been published in the Gateway Writers' five anthologies. Some of her memory pieces have been published in the weekly Ireland's Own *magazine. Also a keen poet, her poems have been published in* The Leader *newspaper. This is Geraldine's second appearance in the* Ireland's Own Anthology.

The Gold Sovereigns

By Muireann Mac Gafraidh,
Athboy, Co. Meath

The family gathered in Granny's parlour after her funeral and Uncle Richard was already inebriated. 'What I want to know is, what happened the gold sovereigns? Father gave Mother a gold sovereign every year and they were married over thirty years. Where are they is what I want to know?' he demanded in a loud cantankerous voice.

DIRECTLY AFTER GRANNY'S funeral, the swarm gathered like locusts into her parlour. They massed and circled into clusters of various family allegiances and grievances of other older times, to drink whiskey, porter and sherry alongside tea and coffee by the gallon. Multifarious family quarrels were examined and autopsied.

I sighed as I looked about me. There they were, for better or worse, MY relatives; the desired and the detested. The large table was laden with enough food to feed a regiment. Silver cutlery and glasses glinted in the reflected light of a chandelier.

'Here child, make yourself useful and go offer these around,' ordered a snotty cousin as she pushed a plate of sandwiches into my hands. I looked at her with disdain. 'Just who do you think you are Peggy O'Sullivan, you're only two years older than me? Don't try and boss me about,' I snapped. I looked at the plate of ham and cheese sandwiches. 'These will do nicely, thanks … Peggy.'

'It's Margaret …' she hissed at me.

I sniggered, and went off to find the lemonade. As I crossed the room I realised one uncle was already mean drunk.

'What I want to know is, what happened the gold sovereigns?'

'Oh don't start that again Richard,' warned my father in a quiet voice.

'I'll say what I like. Father gave Mother a gold sovereign every year and they were married over thirty years. Where are they is what I want to know?' he demanded in a loud cantankerous voice. A malevolent expression conveyed his dark mood.

Aunt Cathleen, or Cait as the family called her, was the youngest and my favourite of all my father's family. She sat collapsed in a fireside chair and stared heartbroken into the smouldering embers of the fire. She looked dreadful, her face looked cold and grey. Her green eyes were red and scalded from tears.

She was a lace maker by profession and also a beautiful pianist but today her fine creative hands just twisted and twisted the lace edged handkerchief in her hands. Richard slithered up to her, leaned on the mantelpiece and sneered down into her face.

'Well, sister dear, where are they? You have been here, alone, with Mother all these years. Waiting, planning for the day... you ... you ... old ... spinster!' he spat.

'Enough I say!' exclaimed great Aunt Cissy.

'Shut up, you old fossil!'

'Rude as ever I see.' she replied unperturbed and took another sip of whiskey and sat back to listen to his expected tirade.

'They were lost in the flood, years ago; the whole area was underwater! Two were found later in a little tin box in the yard. They're gone Richard ... vanished,' sobbed Auntie Cait as she covered her face with tremulous hands.

'Is that so? Well excuse me if I don't believe a word!' he mocked as he paced erratically towards the window that overlooked the back garden.

'She was very fond of her garden though was Mother,' he remarked and stared out into the bleak winter's day. 'Yesss, very fond,' he hissed.

It was true. Granny had loved her garden, especially her prized distinctive flower bed. It was an honest to goodness flower bed as she had used a vast old iron bed frame, painted white, to separate it from the rest of the garden. She had planted it with all her favourite plants.

It was gorgeous in summer with its dolly mixture colours of greens, yellows, pinks and whites of rockery plants alongside golden marigolds, the reds and crimson of Sweet William and the fragrant smell of lavenders and geraniums. The various rocks and stones that surrounded it were whitewashed and it dazzled and danced in the summer sunshine.

Richard pulled out a cigarette from an almost empty packet on the mantelpiece and lit it. He took a deep drag, tapped the box of matches on the knuckles of his left hand and smirked in an unpleasant devious manner. I looked out towards the garden. The day was cold and a thick fog had begun to roll in from the river. The trees were mere dark skeletal forms that drooped as the few lifeless leaves that remained dripped and oozed moisture. I sneezed. My Father suddenly realised I was there. He lifted his arm towards the door.' Go and find your Mother. This is no place for young ears.'

'Aww Dad let me stay, I'll be quiet, honest I will.'

'Go now,' he insisted.

'Please …'

'No. Go … Now.' I knew the tone, it was pointless to argue. I made my way into the hall.

'Grown ups. They thinks they know everything … well they don't!' I muttered to Granny's smokey grey cat 'Sally' as she sat regally on a hall chair. Her mysterious blue eyes returned a look as though she knew many secrets.

'Most of them are stupid asses,' I stated loudly.

'I heard that … get home … now,' came my father's voice.

I grabbed my coat and kicked the umbrella bin hard on my way out. The whole thing collapsed with a clatter. I ran pell mell for home.

It was the day after the funeral. I stared fixedly out our kitchen window. We lived next door to Granny's. I watched as a tall black clad, dark haired figure, cigarette in mouth and a shovel in both hands, attacked the ground with powerful force.

'Mam, why is Uncle Richard digging up Granny's flower bed?' I asked puzzled. My Mother had an angry expression on her face and replied in a dry cryptic tone: 'Who knows? Perhaps he seeks Eldorado.'

I didn't understand what my mother meant. I made a face and shrugged my shoulders and continued to watch fascinated and intrigued as Uncle Richard pushed the shovel into the ground and threw out another shovelful of earth with focused intent. He looked shattered. He scowled, wiped his face with the back of a hairy forearm, spat out the cigarette butt and began again. He did this repeatedly for a long time.

Sometimes he would stop to examine a sod, his fingers clawed and tore at the black wet clay. Occasionally, he barked some invective or other and in a furious manner would throw the clump away. On and on he went until my mother, exasperated, filled the kettle, smacked it onto the stove.

'Go into Auntie Cait and give her a hand and tell Uncle Richard that your Father wants no … would 'like' a word with him please.'

I dashed to the front door as my mother called after me.' And mind your manners!'

Auntie Cait was tidying up her sitting room. There were documents, envelopes of every size and battered dust covered cardboard and tin boxes and dilapidated old handbags strewn all over the place.

'Wow …! What happened?' I gasped.

'Oh! Your Uncle Richard, that's what happened,' came her contemptuous retort as she brushed dust from her skirt.

'What is Uncle Richard looking for?'

'His sense of decency and respect!' she said. She emphasised each word with great care. 'He is an avaricious man!' she declared in disgust.

'What does afca … rick … us mean, Auntie Cait?' Suddenly I stopped, frightened, for just then a dark shadow loomed across the kitchen window and Uncle Richard came into view. His tall, dark, sinister figure filled the doorway. He glared at me.

'Well what do you want brat?' he growled as he threw a shovel back into the garden. It landed with a loud bang and clattered along the concrete path. I jumped, alarmed.

'Enough … you Gurrier! Your brother would like to talk to you,' stated a furious Auntie Cait as she enveloped me in a protective hug.

'Is my dear brother getting a little worried with all my digging? Getting a bit scared that I might find something? Am I getting too close for comfort?' he sneered and headed out the door. I exhaled as the Gurrier left.

'When is he leaving? I don't like him!' I scowled after him.

'Sooner than he thinks pet. How about some biscuits and nice lemonade?'

'Eh, what's Eldorado Auntie Cait?'

'I haven't an iota pet but it sounds foreign.'

'Yeah, I suppose,' I replied and munched on a custard cream.

That was us from that day on; me and Auntie Cait. When I was in trouble, she was my refuge, my quiet safe harbour. I remember back then, in the summers that always seemed sunnier, when my mother called across the gardens for me to come home and do some jobs. I would hide in the giant orange blossom that stood about twenty foot wide and more than ten foot tall, that grew at the bottom of her garden.

I made a deep indented bower, a hideaway among the dense foliage and there I lay among the orange blossom. The cream coloured velvet petals fell about me and on me and onto the pages of a comic or my library books. I was covered in soft luxuriant petals as I read or just day-dreamed about the day I would be a famous and a fearless explorer. I would discover hidden treasures, I would write books about all my terrific adventures and, as I mused, the potent perfume of orange blossom filled the air. To this day I can still recall the sweet wonderful fragrance.

Auntie Cait knew well where I was but never let on. I went everywhere with her after that. We became Butch Cassidy and the Sundance Kid. I was my own 'Hole in the Wall' gang, or rather 'Hole in the Hedge' gang.

I was heartbroken when Auntie Cait passed away. I was handed a letter from her addressed to me in her old shaky hand. It explained much. I followed the instructions she had written in her letter. I went upstairs to her old bedroom and went in search of Granny's battered tin hat box that lived on top of a large, tall wardrobe.

I stood on a rickety white-painted rattan chair and I took down the old shabby and worn black box. Inside was Granny's beloved best hat with the deep brim; it smelled of mothballs. I removed it from its ancient tissue paper and stroked the soft fabric. A silver framed photograph of Granny wearing the self-same hat stood on the dressing table. I gazed into the hat and ran a finger around under the sweat band.

Sure enough, as I had been instructed, I discovered another band of tough, timeworn corded satin lining and … sown into the band were twenty British gold sovereigns. I stood astounded. I held them up to the sunlight that rippled and beamed through the lace curtained window. They glowed and shone, a burnished waterfall. The coins jingled and slipped through my fingers onto the soft eiderdown.

It was a dream come true. I chuckled and also wiped a couple of tears away. 'And I always thought you couldn't keep a secret Auntie Cait.'

Suddenly the room was filled with the wonderful smell of orange blossom.

Let me not forget the villain of this tale, Uncle Richard. My father had a word with Uncle Richard those long years ago. I glimpsed him before he headed for the boat and England. He had an enormous black eye. He later married a widow of means with no children and they lived a very comfortable life in a large house in Birmingham. Like most scoundrels and wastrels he was handsome and liked money, other people's money that is. He never returned and we never met his wife. She outlived him and when he died she had him cremated.

'Well … he always enjoyed a good smoke. I'm sure he smouldered splendidly,' Auntie Cait observed wryly as she blew three smoke rings ceiling-wards when she heard the news. We lifted a glass and saluted the brass framed photograph his wife had sent as a memento and our toast to him was…'To the Gurrier. May he rest in peace!'

Muireann Mac Gafraidh was born and raised in Dublin, and has a grown-up family. Now living in a small village in rural county Meath, she worked abroad for some years. She now works as a part-time Home Care Assistant. She enjoys reading and gardening and, of course, reading Ireland's Own. *She has appeared in quite a few of the* Ireland's Own *anthologies.*

Be Seen and Not Heard

By Sean O'Doherty,
Raheny, Dublin

*On our First Communion Day the altar was festooned with
candles either side of the steps. The place was aglow. Fr. D,
a small slight man, was wearing a surplice at least a size too
big for him. The garment was resplendent with layers of
delicate lace and as we made our way up the steps it
caught fire. There was panic in the church.*

BE SEEN AND not heard! Call it what you like, an
admonition, a caution, or good old-fashioned advice,
the above had to be transcribed into our school head-
liners copies as part of the daily writing routine. We were Rang
a Dó (Second Class) in a small village school on the West Coast.
The headline summed up the strict culture of 1940s Ireland.
You daren't question anything, you never raised your head
above the parapet. It was always silent submission.

Our penmanship was under the watchful eye of our teacher.
We'll call her Mrs. Brightly, or Mrs B for short. Our pens were
small and cumbersome, boasting a tiny filler under the nib.
Even the 12th century scribe, Giraldus Cambrensis, would have
found difficulty filling his parchments with such pesky tools.

The quantity of precious ink varied between meagre and
abundant. The transfer between inkwell and spotless copybook
was hazardous. A blob of ink on a page was fatal and resulted
in a bang on the knuckles from Mrs. B's ruler. Of course the

resulting pain made writing even worse. The Roman alphabet had not come into use. The Gaelic Script demanded 'Síne fadas' (long stroke) and 'buailtes' (full stops) or aspirations. Omissions of these necessary adjuncts to the language always invited instant reprisals from our over-zealous teacher.

I remember in particular the old Gaelic 'g' with its curling end winding back on itself like a greyhound's tail. If you were not careful it was 'bombs away' missing target and splashing dangerously below blue lines. The full stop also came in for pinpoint accuracy. The swollen dot would have been a gift to any espionage agent. Indeed, all the writing procedures were fraught with the fear of 'knuckle dusting.'

Sonny, my school pal, hadn't the greatest co-ordination. His application of pen to paper was more of an attack as a Knight with rusty sword back from the Crusades. There wasn't blood but there was plenty of ink. Teacher pinned the offending piece of literature to Sonny's back. 'Take that home to your parents!' she ordered.

Poor Sonny was upset and humiliated but as soon as Mrs. B disappeared on her bicycle, we removed the offending paper and threw it over the ditch to Mrs Feely's goat. We knew that the goat would eat anything but we didn't wait around to find out.

First Holy Communion was a major event in the school and local community. Rows of girls in immaculate white dresses were flanked by the boys in traditional navy blue suits. But the preliminaries to the gala day were scary.

At seven years of age we had to examine our conscience and recall a few 'sins' or misdemeanours. For about an hour or so I wrestled with my conscience and failed to produce any guilty offence. Eventually, Mrs. B put me into the cloakroom, which became known as the 'sin bin'. At last it had the desired effect and I came up with something to satisfy my conscience.

This prepared me for another session in a cold dark confession box. Fr. D hadn't great patience with the children. 'Speak up,' he'd say. 'I can't hear you.'

He didn't seem shocked by the baring of my soul. My pal Sonny was next and he looked very worried. 'It will be okay,' I assured him. 'He's a bit deaf but he's very nice, you just have to speak up!'

Soon the last pupil had finished the formalities and we all trouped to school with a joy in our step.

As Rural Electrification hadn't reached our outpost we had to rely on candles and oil lamps for illuminations. On the big day the altar was festooned with candles either side of the steps. The place was aglow. Fr. D, a small slight man, was wearing a surplice at least a size too big for him.

The garment was resplendent with layers of delicate lace and as we made our way up the steps it caught fire. There was panic in the Church. But the quick-thinking sacristan rushed out and wrapped the poor cleric in a dusty old moth eaten rug. Everyone knew there was no love lost between the two pr-otagonists and we watched him give the priest an extra roll in the old rug, just in case.

There was still more drama ahead on our special day. We usually sailed our boats on a little pond near our home in the afternoons. As I launched my little boat into the waters, the wind whipped the sails. Reaching across to steady it, I fell head-long into the stagnant pond while dressed in my new suit, white starched shirt, ribbons and badge.

There was no life-saving sacristan to hand so I just floundered about in the water. I eventually made it to the edge and was unrecognisable when I staggered in home.

School trundled on. We were in the middle of an Irish class one day when, due to something akin to metal fatigue, Teacher's cane broke. I was given the job of procuring a substitute 'bata' or stick. She beckoned me to her desk. 'Take a branch off a tree outside,' she ordered.

The big sycamore was outside the school wall. I ventured on my task, climbing the wall and swinging 'Tarzan like' to land on a branch. The branch broke on me and both branch and I landed on the ground. I grabbed the branch and the next movement was to scale the wall.

Army like, I threw the weapon over and clambered after it. Darting down the path I imagined myself leading a band of top commandoes on a secret mission to capture enemy head-quarters. I was just about to issue orders to attack when the castle doors, sorry, 'school doors,' opened and Mrs B appeared.

'What kept you?' she snapped. Once inside the classroom she pared down the stick, removing all bark, branch endings and leaves, then smoothing it down with sandpaper. 'Wouldn't like to get a belt of that!' Sonny confided to me.

Teacher threw a question at me. Whether it was the fact that I had just personally endangered life and limb to find a stick, I had thought I was immune from punishment that day. I was dumbfounded when I got two of her best on my open palm. Smooth stick but rough justice.

School life moved on from those early infant days and we completed our Primary Certificate. Then the spidery writing gave way to tentative taps on the typewriter and much later, progression to the keyboard.

Job opportunities were scarce in Ireland at the time and many of our classmates had to emigrate abroad. The rest of us chose to embrace the 'old reliables' like the civil service, the gardaí or the teaching profession.

My dear pal Sonny became a missionary and by that time he had truly mastered the art of writing. Preaching to his faithful flock he was both seen and heard.

Sean O'Doherty from Raheny in Dublin is appearing in the Ireland's Own Anthology *for the third time. He was a prize winner in the Memories section 2012 with* A Teller of Tales *and he had a short story published entitled* Harvested *in 2012, an amusing tale about a city dweller helping out with the harvest during the World War 2 National Emergency.*

The Listeners

By Rosemary Daly,
Drumconrath, Co. Meath

*Old Jimmy was having constant rows with his family and he
decided to return up the hill to his former home, long since derelict.
The cottage had housed nothing but rats and spiders and an
occasional few cattle for more than thirty years, but he lodged himself under the arch of the chimney breast. Here he would remain
and finish out his days in his own home place, he decided …*

THERE HAD BEEN another row, worse than the usual. 'I'll not stay down there below no more. That's it now!' He shook his fist at them. 'I'll not be told what to do by anyone.' The elderly man had then trudged the few hundred yards up the little drumlin to his own former home, a cottage, long since derelict.

He had made his way into the one big room of the old house and had lodged himself under the arch of the chimney breast. Here, he decided, he would remain and finish out his days in his own home place.

The cottage had housed nothing but rats and spiders and an occasional few cattle for more than thirty years, and the old man now sat marooned under the chimney breast which offered the only shelter. Drops of rain began to pick at the tin roof, more and more of them until their plinking and pinging cried a steady metallic dirge above him. The rusting tin let in the water to pitt pitt pitt on the cottage floor.

At first she had followed him and had stood in front of him, her fists on her hips, her face fattened with temper. Her voice was as loud as his own.

'If your mother could only hear you now,' he'd said to her.

'Listen to yourself!' she'd shot back at him. 'I suppose she'd have been proud of you as well. Sittin' up here like a spoiled child expectin' everyone to feel sorry for you!'

'Go way and lave me alone.'

'Listen,' she snorted then. 'I came up here to talk to you.'

'YOU listen!' he'd shouted. 'Nobody listens to me!'

The old man remained steadfast. This would be his home from now on. He should never have left it in the first place and let them talk him into that house down there below.

'Right so. Stay here then!' she roared at him finally and she turned towards the door, paused, and added, 'I just don't care any more.'

And then she was gone.

He could hear her muttering to herself fainter and fainter as she went away back down the hill.

A while later she had sent up Himself. Useless lump.

He had stood himself just inside the door, well away from him, and he had said what she had told him to say. About how he'd have to see things from their point of view. He'd have to tell them where he was going. And when. And how they'd had the whole neighbourhood out looking for him.

Did they think he was a child?

And he only after going across the Tobberfinan Lane to the Gael Fitzsimons' house to see the new grey cob that he was after buying in Ballybay, that he was telling everyone was really a stallion and all about the great twist he was after doing on the dealer from Clones.

The state the Gael's was in! The windows were all black dirty and there was a big padlock on the door. On the door! What were they thinking! The yard was covered in yellowy grass and, best of all, the flower bed out along the lane where the Gael's old mother grew the orange lilies to annoy the priest was all full of nettles! Wait till he saw the Gael. Nettles! He'd give him some ribbing over that!

He had gone all around the house but he couldn't find a way in. There was no sign of anyone. Neither was there any sign of the new cob which he had expected to find in Big Mac's Field at the side of the turf shed. And so, after he poked about a bit more, picking at the flaking blisters of paint and rubbing puzzled fingers over the rust reddened hinges and locks, he had set off home again.

It was only on his way back that he remembered that the Gael was dead this forty years and more. And sure why wouldn't he be? Sure wasn't he a good twenty years older than himself!

The Lump was still there in front of him now. Still bleating. Why didn't she at least marry a proper man! He didn't even give her chick nor child.

Listen to him! He would have to 'see sense'. She's 'worried' about him!

Worried! Worried was the last thing she was. Delighted to be rid of him more like. Well, now she was. He'd show the whole lot of them. He'd live right here from now on. Independent.

When his son-in law had run out of steam he backed out of the cottage and melted away back down the hill. It seemed that the old man's resolve was even greater than their powers of persuasion. Several hours passed and there was no sign of him coming down the hill. So they held a meeting to plan what to do next. But none of them could think of anything. He was pure stubborn. When he was in this sort of mood he'd listen to nobody.

Hours went by. Heavy rain began to fall. It was getting serious now. He'd catch his death.

Eventually, late into the evening, when everyone had gone home with their concern, an elderly neighbour made his way up to the cottage. The man entered the darkening room and picked his way over to the hearth where the old man was still wedged in beneath the chimney breast. He sat hunched over now, his elbows on his knees, while the rain dripped miserably in the gloom growing around him.

'I heard you were up here.'

The new arrival settled himself carefully on the narrow ledge alongside the old man, stretched out one leg and pulled out from his trousers pocket a flattened box of Woodbines. He set two cigarettes on his lower lip, touched a match to them and pulled deeply. Then he turned and handed one of the cigarettes to his companion. The old man took it, looked straight at the giver and said,

'I'll not give in Tommy. I will not!'

'Aye,' said his companion, nodding his head contemplatively.

The two men sat side by side staring out at the black mud of the old cottage floor. They each pulled and sighed to their own rhythm. Crows that had settled in the old abandoned chimney shuffled above them, kraaking irritably at the disturbance to their damp slumber.

The rain had got more noticeable and was making its way down the wide chimney that was open to the sky above. It was steadily dampening the shoulders of the two men. Grey blue smoke curled itself upwards from their yellow fingers, turning when it hit the overhanging arch and swirling back down and around them again.

They leaned back now into the once whitewashed wall where the overhang offered a little protection. They sat awkwardly, the flaking lime whitening their backs. A wind had got up and soon some complaining sheet of tin on the roof screeked rhythmically above them. The branches of overgrown elder trees stirred outside, tipping and scraping at what was left of the windows.

The old man stared into the darkened room before him where generations of his people had lived out their lives. He saw people now before him where he knew well there were no people any more. All of them moving and living and taking shape through the smoke in front of him.

And his own child, his only child.

A little girl in a blue dress smiled up at him now from where she was playing, her fair hair atumble,

'Dadda, listen down the chimleys!' She played on the floor in front of him with the dolls' house he had made for her.

He had made the toy for her when she was about five. Painstakingly, he had copied the plans that he had got his brother to send to him from America. He had worked at it over the long winter nights outside in the shed under the light of a paraffin lamp. When he had it cobbled together as best he could, himself and his wife had made a trip to Dublin where they bought furniture for the inside of the house. They had even bought two small, naked dolls that his wife later sewed clothes for.

He stuck on grey wallpaper to make a roof and he slotted in a chimney with red pipes. It was the chimney that mostly fascinated his daughter.

She had played for endless quiet hours with the dolls' house, lost in the lives she created for the two dolls that lived in it. The whole front of the house opened back on hinges so that all the rooms, and what she decided went on in them, were all under her gaze at the same time.

She loved moving the two dolls from room to room, telling them how good they were, how much she loved them or sending them to bed early for being naughty. The dolls were both her sisters and her children and she lovingly watched over the lives she made for them.

But on the outside of the house was the chimney and, after her mother had closed up her playtime and had latched it, she would put her ear to the rim of the chimney pipes or poke her wee fingers down them, as if she might still access the closed house and keep order on the two dolls whose lives still carried on within it.

'Listen Dadda!' she would whisper up to him, the side of the blonde head stuck to the chimney pots.

'They're in bed now. But they're not asleep. They're still talking. I can hear them.' Wide eyed and with her ear pressed to the chimney she would recount to him the details of the dolls' hushed conversations.

He could still see her now, poking her tiny fingers down the round red pipes of the dolls' house.

'Listen down the chimleys, Dadda!'

Sometimes she would beg him so beseechingly to listen and he would kneel down on the floor and put his ear to the little chimney pots. 'Are they crying Dadda? Are they sad?'

To please her he would nod in great seriousness and pretend to hear the little dolls weeping below him.

'I will have to go and tell them not to be sad' she would declare. And she would beg her mother to unlatch the little house again so that she could hold her dolls one more time and tell them how much she loved them.

'Listen Dadda.'

The blue smoke released itself on a long, heavy breath, and he shook his head, lost to the pictures.

'Aye,' said Tommy, as if he could read the old man's mind.

The wind moaned outside the cottage walls and rain wept continually now down the chimney.

Tommy once again produced the lulling comfort of the Woodbines. By the time the fifth cigarette each had been pulled to its end, several hours had passed. It was cold. The fire of the old man's temper had died in him and now the old cottage came whispering to him.

'Listen Dadda. Listen.'

He watched as Tommy tossed a last butt onto the cottage floor and stretched his two legs out slowly in front of him, yawned widely and pushed his arms outwards until the bones in his wrists clicked.

'I think, Jimmy, we'll head down below,' he said.

The old man looked around him. He looked at what was in front of him. Silence and emptiness. What on earth were the two of them doing smoking fags up here in the cold?

'For sure!' he replied. 'It's right dark. And sure Mary'll be wondering where I am.'

And the two neighbours got stiffly to their feet, stooped out from under the chimney breast and crossed the cottage floor. They walked carefully down the hill together to the house where the old man's daughter sat motionless in the darkness of her kitchen.

Listening.

Rosemary Daly grew up in Bective, Co. Meath, just a stone's throw from the home of Mary Lavin, her childhood inspiration. She now lives in Drumconrath, Co. Meath. She is a teacher by profession and, as well as writing, she enjoys reading and music and is also a well-known exhibitor and judge of pedigree show dogs.

Grosse Île – A Message of Kinship

BY BRENDAN LANDERS,
MARIAN PARK, BALDOYLE, DUBLIN

The island of Grosse Île is a sacred place and we could feel it in our bones. We walked and talked softly on it. Our ancestors came there in droves to escape from the ravages of the Great Famine and in hope for a better life. For many of them the island became their graveyard. My visit had a profound impact on me …

EMIGRATION CAN PLAY havoc with a person's sense of belonging and people respond in various ways to the discombobulation this can entail. Some people remain resolutely Irish no matter how long they are away. Others embrace the new place whole-heartedly and easily cast off the psychological and emotional trappings of their Irishness.

And others reach a stage in their cultural osmosis in which their sense of identity shifts and becomes enmeshed in the phenomenon of separation. I belong to that third category and I remember to the day the moment in which the shift became evident to me.

It was a blustery, rainy day in 1994 when Ireland's then President, Mary Robinson, visited Grosse Île, a small island on the St. Lawrence River in Quebec, where thousands of victims of the Irish Famine are buried. I travelled with a busload of pilgrims from Toronto where I'd been living for 10 years. We

194

spent the night in a hotel in the town of Trois-Rivières and rose at dawn to travel by ferry to the island.

We were accompanied on the trip by representatives of the Ancient Order of Hibernians, the Gaelic Athletic Association, Comhaltas Ceóltóirí Éireann, Concern and a myriad of Irish-American and Irish-Canadian associations. People came from places as far-flung as Montreal, Chicago, New York, Boston, New Orleans, Belfast, Dublin, and even the Kanesataki First Nations' reserve in Quebec.

On approaching the island, the first thing we saw was a Celtic Cross, 46 feet tall, overlooking the St. Lawrence from the top of Telegraph Hill, the highest point on the island. It was erected by the Ancient Order of Hibernians in 1909, back when the Great Famine was more immediate in the memory of Irish émigrés.

The island is a sacred place and we could feel it in our bones. We walked and talked softly on it. Our ancestors came there in droves to escape from the ravages of the Great Famine and in hope for a better life. For many of them, Gross Île became their graveyard. Some Quebecois now call the place the Isle of Irish Sorrows. Others call it simply the Irish Island.

There are broad meadows at both ends of the island where the migrants are buried, 'stacked like cordwood' in the words of one contemporary observer. Before the end of May 1847, Dr. Douglas, the medical superintendent of Grosse Île, was reporting between 50 and 60 deaths per day. By June 5 the death toll had tripled. At the end of that year Dr. Douglas erected a monument on the island to commemorate the four doctors and two lay people who had died caring for the sick.

The monument bears this inscription:

> *In this secluded spot lie the mortal remains of 5424 persons who fleeing from Pestilence and Famine in Ireland in the year 1847 found in America but a grave.*

The earth atop the mass graves was of a spongy, ductile texture. As my foot sank into it I felt like jerking back. I wished I could glide over the graveyard and not disturb it. But at the same time there was a magnetic aura to it that had made me want to touch it or a part of it. I wanted to feel the grass, put my hand on one of the army of white wooden crosses, pluck a flower, say a prayer. I wanted to do something – anything – to respond to the message of kinship I was receiving from this haunted place.

The final ceremony of the day was a laying of wreaths at the Celtic Cross on the top of Telegraph Hill. Back down on the docks it was now raining heavily and the pilgrims gathered for departure, soaked to the skin but spiritually edified. A man with an accordion played the Fury Brothers song *Steal Away*.

Early the next morning I boarded the bus for the long trip back to Toronto. I sat alone, as did many others. The island had impressed us profoundly and we were not yet ready to let go of the intensity of the experience.

About halfway back to Toronto I realised that my visit to Grosse Île had triggered, or at least hurried along, a shift in my sense of self. I was like Dorothy in Oz with the reality dawning on her that she was not in Kansas anymore. I was no longer just Irish. Somehow, over the course of my decade-long odyssey in Canada, like many another expatriate, my perception of my Irishness had shifted and my visit to Grosse Île had clarified my new sense of self.

We who have shifted see ourselves and our Irishness through a prism that has been embellished by an awareness of alternative realities and possibilities. We embody a sense of separateness that contains togetherness. We belong to Ireland and beyond. We are of the diaspora.

Brendan Landers is an award-winning journalist, short story writer and novelist. He was born and grew up in Dublin. In 1984 he emigrated to Toronto, where he lived for 17 years. He is now based back in Dublin. His short fiction has won many prizes in Ireland and in Canada and his journalism has been published in a wide variety of Irish, British, Canadian and US publications. He is former Publisher/Managing Editor of Ireland's Eye, *a magazine for Irish Canadians, and the former Editor of the* Irish Canada News, *a Toronto-based monthly newspaper. He has written for a number of other publications in New York, Australia, the UK, and Canada. His website is: www.brendanlanders.com*

Heroes

By Alan Egan,
Ballinlough, Cork

'Introducing, in the red corner, at two hundred and five pounds, from Battersea England, the heavyweight champion of the British Empire, wearing black trunks – Don Cockell. In the blue corner, from Boston Massachusetts, weighing one hundred and eighty-nine pounds, wearing white trunks, the heavyweight champion of the world – Rocky Marciano.'

IRELAND IN THE early 1950s was a pretty bleak place, a place where any self-respecting young fella needed a hero. Or three. There was Dad of course, and Uncle Mick with his All-Ireland medals, and Uncle Joe who fought in the war. But the really classy ones came from elsewhere, especially from the world of sport.

A young fella knew these sportsmen for their skill, for their courage, and most of all for their victories. Christy Ring, naturally. For a little god is he, on the north side of the Lee. Beyond Cork though, choices were scarce. The Football League in England was as dour as be-damned, even though we always tuned in to the scratchy BBC Light Programme to get the First Division results. *Portsmouth, nil; Manchester United, nil.*

There were films too, and books, and comics … *Biggles, Flash Gordon, Dan Dare.* But sure they were only makey-uppy. A fella would still be searching for a true king of the world.

Boxing was big, glamorous and dangerous. And boxing had world champions. But forget about the bantams, the feathers, the middleweights. Heavyweights, now they were the lads. And Rocky Marciano was the daddy of them all. Undefeated.

May the sixteenth, 1955 was a Monday, a normal schoolday, to be followed by another normal schoolday on Tuesday. So it came as a bit of a surprise after tea when Dad said,

'Have you much homework?'

'The usual', I said, wondering why he asked.

'Get it done quick so,' he said, 'there's something I want to tell you later.'

And then he winked.

That was strange, but I got the ecker done sharpish. Dad was helping Mam to put the baby to bed. He was only a few weeks old, my new little brother that is, and Dad was all smiles. That was a bit strange too, especially as he was always telling Mam that he was well out of practice dealing with babies and the like. But he got him settled, and while Mam was still upstairs, he brought me out to the kitchen. All hush-hush like.

'How would you feel about getting up at half-three?' he asked.

'What?'

'Yeah, don't worry, I'll call you. But you'll have to promise to be quiet'.

I didn't know what to make of this and all sorts of things were going through my head, but Dad was grinning from ear to ear.

'The fight is on the radio', he said, 'at four o'clock. All the way from San Francisco. And it'll only be eight o'clock this evening there'.

The penny dropped. Rocky Marciano and Don Cockell, the big English fella. Dad had shown me their photos in the *Sunday Independent*. Champion and Challenger.

'Yep', said Dad. 'And it's Eamonn Andrews who will be doing the commentary.'

I didn't hear him coming into my bedroom, but there was Dad, finger to his lips, with my dressing-gown in his hand.

Downstairs, the clock showed ten to four, there were four biscuits on a plate, the kettle was on, the radio was on. But turned down low. We had a Pye radio, one of the ones with a 'magic eye'. That was a green-ish thing for tuning in. It flickered open and shut when the signal got bad or good. I reckoned we'd need it. The BBC Light Programme was long wave, I knew that, and the reception was always dodgy.

'Well, who are you for?' asked Dad, as he warmed the teapot and put two big spoons of Barry's tea into it, ready for the boiling water.

Without waiting for an answer, he went on: 'Some of the lads in work think we should support Cockell. He's from London and God knows there's enough Irishmen over there right now trying to earn a crust. And he's definitely the underdog. Sure we all love the underdog, don't we? Except of course if it's Cork they're playing. But, anyway. Who're you for?'

'Rocky Marciano,' I said.

'Ah, good lad,' he said, and he gave me a mock punch to the chin.

A mock right hook, it was. Dad had shown me how to lead, normal or southpaw, how to duck and weave. The different punches, jabs, hooks, straights, uppercuts. 'Keep your guard up.' That was his favourite thing to say.

The tea and biscuits were long gone by the time the fight was over. Mam had come down to warm a bottle for the baby. Dad and me were hunched over next to the radio, trying to hear Eamonn Andrews through the crackles. Mam looked at us, looked at the clock, shook her head, said nothing, and went back up again.

It was close enough at the start, the fight that is. Then, after a few rounds, Rocky Marciano got on top, but Cockell wouldn't go down. Eamonn Andrews seemed to think that every round would be the last, but it wasn't. I thought that was great. I wanted it to keep going, I didn't care how late, so long as Rocky Marciano won. Eventually, the referee stopped it, in the ninth. A TKO (technical knock out). I knew what that was. Rocky Marciano was still the champ. Still undefeated. And I went to bed happy.

Next morning I was jaded tired, but I still had to get up for school. A lot of the lads were talking about Rocky Marciano, but there was no mention of anyone getting up to listen to it. So I didn't say anything either. Some of them wouldn't believe you anyway.

Dad brought the *Examiner* home at teatime. Dad always read the *Examiner*. He folded one page over and pointed out where it said that this was the first ever live broadcast from America to Britain.

'And we were up to hear it,' he said, 'you and me. Always remember that.'

Then he showed me another paragraph further down about how brave Cockell was. He was a blacksmith from Battersea, it said, and he was more than a stone heavier than Rocky Marciano. But Rocky Marciano was faster and stronger and could punch a lot harder, so Cockell hadn't much hope of winning. Down at the end of the page, where it said Reuters, was a bit saying that, in the changing room before the start, Cockell had asked the referee, 'No matter what happens, don't stop the fight.'

So it went on far too long until the referee finally did have to stop it. I didn't know what to make of this. Dad said that Cockell got an awful lot of money even though he lost, but I still wondered why he kept going for so long. Maybe he just didn't have any common sense. Dad was always going on about using your common sense. But I still couldn't figure it out.

The next day, Dad had the *Examiner* at teatime again. He

read one bit out loud and later gave it to me to read for myself. It said the Americans held the fight in San Francisco because the rules in California were different. So the ring they used was much smaller than usual and this was a big help to the harder hitter. And there was another rule only in California, it said, that a boxer couldn't be disqualified even if he kept punching the other boxer below the belt.

But the main article in the *Examiner* was all about what the American sports reporters had written in their papers. And, clear as day, they said that Marciano broke nearly every rule in the book. He hit Don Cockell after the bell, they said, he used his head and his elbows, punched him below the belt loads of times, and once even hit him when he was down. But the referee didn't even give him a warning. Not a single one.

They said that Don Cockell had no chance at all.

Dad cut out that report and kept it for ages, and sometimes I used to get it out and read it. The more I read it, I still couldn't decide if Don Cockell was really brave to take all of this, maybe out of respect for himself and his supporters, or if he actually was stupid. But I got to thinking maybe that Don Cockell might be more of a hero than Marciano.

There was talk that there would be a re-match in London, but that never happened. A few months later Marciano had another title fight, and knocked out Archie Moore. I don't know if it was on the radio or not but Dad never said anything about getting up to listen to it. Marciano gave up boxing after that. He had forty-nine fights altogether, and won the forty-nine of them. He retired in 1956. Undefeated.

'But not untarnished.' Dad said, 'not to my mind anyway.'

I learned a lot from having Rocky Marciano as a hero. For one thing, I got to sit with Dad in the kitchen, in the small hours of a May morning, eating Lincoln Creams as slowly as I could, listening to Eamonn Andrews on the radio. But the main thing I realised was that a fella had to pick his heroes carefully. That you might be better off to stick to just three. Like Dad, and Uncle Mick, and Uncle Joe.

Alan Egan is a native of Cork city. He is fascinated by Cork's diverse history, and by the array of characters who daily walk its streets. In 2003, after a long career in the business world, he became a student at UCC where he completed a primary and a master's degree. During this time he also documented his grandfather's contribution to public life in Cork. Alan joined a writers group in 2015 and began to write fiction and short stories in addition to local history and family pieces. In 2018, he was invited to read at the Cork International Short Story Festival. Alan and his wife Ger have four children and seven grandchildren.

The Christmas Cat

By Paul McDermott,
Servite Court, Liverpool

*An unexpected 'guest' arrives at the front door on Christmas Eve,
invites himself in after checking out the hosts and the premises,
and makes himself at home for the Festive season.*

H E WASN'T MUCH to look at. He had clearly been 'round the block' more than once, certainly been in a few scraps, but the fact that he turned up at the door that Christmas Eve suggested that he had won more fights than he'd lost.

The first sign of his advent was a distinguished *miaow* which was neither petulant nor demanding, but had a fine echo in the hallway outside our second-floor apartment. I choose my adjectives carefully. You may well ask, how can a cat's 'voice' be described as 'petulant' or even 'demanding'? And as for suggesting it can 'sound distinguished' even before you have the faintest idea of what this unexpected Christmas guest might look like …

Only a true *aficionado* of all things feline would understand.

When I opened the door, he was sitting neatly on the doormat. He looked up, calmly met my gaze, and then glanced beyond me as if inspecting the property. He actually appeared to nod his approval. I automatically took a half-pace to one side and caught myself making a gesture of welcome with my free hand.

We were young, in love, and wouldn't have noticed (or cared) if green snow had fallen from the clouds which were 'sky-blue-pink with a finny haddock border' as my Gran would have called them. Nothing was going to spoil our first Christmas. Of course we took him in; how could anyone refuse at such a special time of year?

We guessed he'd been living wild for some time. His fur was thick, excellent insulation against the merciless Scandinavian winter, but well cared for, free from tats and uneven clumps. He seemed to be a 'healthy' weight, neither starved nor carrying a paunch.

He padded around the living room, and purred his approval of everything he saw. His nostrils quivered with unmistakeable pleasure as he brushed his cheek along the lowest branches of our small pine tree, and made no undue fuss when we gently towelled him dry. He even stood patient and stock-still when my girlfriend used a low setting on her hair dryer to complete the job.

We'd bought enough food to feed an army – who doesn't, over Christmas and New Year? – so, one more (small) mouth to feed wasn't going to be a problem. But as every shop in Denmark had closed at midday, we had to hope he was house-trained. Fortified by a plateful of fresh tuna, which was washed down by a modest portion of cream, he blinked his thanks (Yes, cats DO communicate their feelings in many subtle ways) and then proceeded to give us our next lesson in Felistic Service by leading us to the door and gazing meaningfully once more into my eyes.

I knew what was expected of me, and watched myself take the key and open the door. He headed for the stairwell: a glance over his regal right shoulder was an imperial request (as opposed to an 'imperious demand') for us to accompany him.

We followed, down two flights of stairs and to the rear door of the property which gave onto a small grassed area – 'garden' would have been an optimistic estate agent's exaggeration. A discreet scratch against the wall, where snow had not piled as deep, and the final necessity of nature had been accomplished.

There was only one matter we couldn't resolve immediately. What would happen if we were to risk leaving a total stranger of a cat on his own in the house while we went to Midnight Mass? We talked it over, and decided to trust him. The church was only a few streets away, after all, perhaps five or six hundred metres, and round four corners.

Ninety minutes later, when we left the service, he was sat on the top step of the church porch, licking his paws, ready to escort us home. I am absolutely certain I checked the windows and locked the door.

We hadn't planned for or expected family visitors, and we weren't disappointed. We hadn't long moved in, and barely knew our neighbours. Our unexpected guest was more than welcome, and we enjoyed his company as much as I hope he enjoyed ours.

He played with the decorations on the tree and anywhere else within his reach, resembling the childish delight of a kitten (though I estimate he'd seen at least a dozen winters). For the next three days we took enormous pleasure from entertaining him and giving him our undivided attention.

We even started discussing the naming of this particular cat. It is, of course, a pointless fantasy to imagine any mere mortal can ever learn any cat's one, ineffable, particular name.

Late on New Year's Eve he made his by-now well recognised signal that he wished to attend to his evening toiletries.

The purr and the 'come hither' glance at the top of the stair was without doubt deeper, longer, and more sincere than on any previous occasion. We followed, as had become the custom, and stood in the doorway, respecting his privacy.

Looking back, I think we already knew what was about to happen, but that didn't make it any easier or less heart-rending. This time, when he'd carefully and conscientiously buried his waste, he sat bolt upright and gave us the longest, loudest purr he'd produced during the whole of our brief acquaintanceship.

Turning around, with a magnificent tail bushed ramrod-straight and vertical he headed without haste to the bottom of the garden. There he took a graceful running leap, landing for a split-second on the top of the fence before disappearing into the night and out of our lives.

Paul McDermott was born in Liverpool in 1950 (the Chinese Year of the Tiger). A feline instinct to roam led him to pursue a teaching career as a wandering 'Supply Teacher' throughout Europe, mostly in Scandinavia and north Germany. Having always 'scribbled his thoughts', he began writing full time when he retired and came home to care for his father. Currently he has five books in print, three for adults and two for children, and two more are due for release in the near future. One of the adult books, The Chapel of Her Dreams, *was reviewed in* Ireland's Own *and it forms the first volume of a fictional trilogy based on the history of the Roscommon sept of the Clan McDermott. He has also contributed poetry and prose to a number of anthologies, and he has also scripted plays for local amateur drama groups.*

Waiting for the Bus

By Freda Cave,
Annalong, Newry, Co. Down

Upon retirement, Olive made the brave decision to transplant her life with her husband, Ronnie, from bustling Liverpool to the tranquil West of Ireland backwater of Corcreelin, despite dire warnings from her concerned sister. All went well until Ronnie died suddenly and she was left to cope on her own …

OLIVE STOOD IN FRONT of her long mirror surveying her appearance. She really wanted to look her best for today's outing but without anyone to advise her, she wasn't sure if lilac was her colour. Although it did suit her silvery hair and fair complexion she thought. She'd taken the bus into town the day before to buy her new outfit, and been lucky to find a pretty little bag and strappy shoes with a vanilla sheen to them, to complement her skirt and twinset.

Olive felt a twinge of nerves. She wouldn't know everyone on the community minibus that was due to call for her. In fact she knew very few from around here except perhaps to see, and to have a vague idea of where they lived in the village. She hadn't even been aware of a weekly ladies circle before getting into conversation with the woman who drove the local minibus, who also happened to be in the post office when Olive was collecting her pension.

'We meet in the old boathouse at the pier and are always glad to see a new member, so maybe you'd like to come along on a

Thursday if you're free,' Joan had suggested. 'In fact, we're going on a mystery shopping trip next week, why not join us?'

'I'd like to,' Olive had shyly accepted, and Joan said the bus would pick her up at her own door about ten thirty on Thursday morning.

Olive walked home on a cloud, thrilled at having been asked. It had been a long time since she had felt included anywhere and she chose to pretend that it didn't matter. It did matter; the reality was that Olive was lonely. Her own fault, she thought ruefully; she wasn't very good at pushing herself forward, she'd always been the sort to hang on the periphery and to wait to be drawn in. Her late husband had been the extrovert; her frontman, she used to tease him, but after he had died Olive discovered how much closer to the truth that had been than she realised.

Ronnie and she had always loved their camper van holidays touring Ireland, and once they discovered the tranquil backwater of Corcreelin they left a little bit of their hearts there each time they went home. Home was Liverpool, where they'd been born, bred, and lived all their lives without a thought of uprooting before this little West coast village began calling to them. Once Ronnie took early retirement the temptation to answer that call grew ever stronger, and when a house along the shore front came up for sale it was the deciding factor for making their home in the place that had stolen their hearts.

'You're mad. Totally bonkers,' Olive's sister had exploded. 'At your age, moving to where you don't even know anyone. Everything you've ever known is here; neighbourhood, friends, and family!'

'What family Ella?' Olive queried. 'I only have you and your family. We're still early sixties, flexible enough to adapt. We'll make new friends and we have each other.'

'You're taking a lot for granted. You may not settle there, you're a suburban dweller. You'll miss your trips to the city centre and your shopping malls, then there's your social life; and what, God forbid, if anything should happen to either of you and the other is left alone?' Ella asked.

Her sister must have had a crystal ball, Olive reflected bitterly. Ronnie had integrated quickly into village society, joining the locals for a pint in the pub, befriending the fishermen down at the pier. He had even talked animatedly about investing in a little boat with an outboard motor so that he could do a bit of fishing, and never idle, had begun renovating their old barn to a mini-gym before Ella's warning had become stark reality just two years after settling into their new home.

Ronnie dropped dead before his sixty-fifth birthday. His sudden passing had left Olive desolate and sent shockwaves through the village, with people finding it hard to believe; a relatively young man, so vibrant and well liked, suddenly gone. Neighbours were kind and quick to rally round but much as their support was appreciated, Olive was relieved when Ella arrived to supervise the funeral arrangements. Ella was the one born with the efficiency gene and Olive let her take over while, as always, she gratefully retreated to the background.

'Well, you can hardly live here now by yourself. You'll want to start making plans to come back home,' Ella announced the day following Ronnie's funeral.

'I am home,' Olive returned, her brow furrowed.

'Oh don't be ridiculous,' Ella snorted, 'this was a pipedream; it was never a practical move at your age dear, admit it. I mean, did you even have a say in the matter? It seems to me that everything Ronnie did, you blindly followed.'

For a minute Olive fought back tears.

'Yes, of course I followed; but not blindly Ella,' she finally managed to say. 'I loved Ronnie and of course I followed him gladly because he wouldn't have taken me if I didn't want to go. So I will stay here with him, where I know he wished to be laid to rest.'

Ella was speechless; her sister wasn't usually so assertive. But she didn't argue; nor was the matter ever discussed again before she left in the hire car she had picked up at the airport; an incredible accomplishment to Olive's mind, who couldn't drive their ride-on lawnmower let alone plan and negotiate a journey involving an airline ticket.

Ronnie had done all that sort of thing and now she would have to learn how to deal with things like banking and household accounts. Olive had been content in her kitchen trying out a new recipe, doing a crossword or sitting at her sewing machine, happy to let Ronnie carry on with any of the official looking paperwork that she didn't understand.

In the year since he'd passed, Olive had managed to cope. Neighbours had been kind, inviting her to lunch, offering to take her shopping or help with her garden, but all they could do was ask and when met with a hesitant Olive, people assumed she preferred to be left alone. In fact, without Ronnie, it was uncertainty that held her back. She wanted to be accepted, to join in and be part of village life the way Ronnie had and she tried to find the courage to integrate, but Olive didn't have Ronnie's easy confidence to blend into company.

And now, dressed in her new clothes and stiff from sitting at her window waiting for the bus, Olive knew she should never have allowed herself to feel so enthusiastic about today as she smarted with humiliation and disappointment. They had forgotten her; the bus was gone nearly two hours ago and her absence probably not even noticed. No-one had ever really noticed her, apart from Ronnie, she reflected; who else had time for a timid woman with no great personality. Forlornly, she peeled off her new clothes and hung them in the wardrobe; she hadn't been sure that lilac was her colour anyway.

Back into her navy skirt and blouse, Olive noticed her cat sitting on the window sill. It had been a great source of comfort, this little stray that had arrived one morning last year on her doorstep, hungry and thirsty. That's all any creature wanted, a drink and a bite to eat, Olive pondered as she watched her new friend enjoy what she set down for it. But it hadn't gone away afterwards, instead deciding to live with Olive. She would nip up to the mini market on the Main Street for more cat food Olive thought, while there was still the chance of avoiding the return of the minibus bus and the embarrassment of bumping into Joan. But bump into Joan she did.

'Olive,' Joan boomed, 'I was just going to call round to see you if that's convenient.'

'There's no need, really. There will be other trips,' Olive stammered, 'I had things to do today anyway.'

'You mean the shopping trip? Olive, that's tomorrow; I said Thursday sweetheart. This is Wednesday,' Joan chuckled.

'Oh how silly of me, of course it is,' Olive flustered.

'Did you really think we'd go without you? What I wanted to see you about is nothing to do with the bus trip. Can I come round for ten minutes?' Joan asked.

Olive was intrigued. And pleased, as she added a vanilla sponge cake to her shopping basket; she was having a visitor to her house for a cup of tea.

'Well then, you're wondering why I'm here,' Joan stated, sipping her tea. 'To be honest I'm hoping you can help out. It's just that some of the local ladies would be interested in forming a choral group. But we have no pianist? I know you can play Olive, I hear you whenever I walk my dog past your house in the evenings.'

'Well I do, but …' Olive gasped, her face pink with confusion.

'It's a shame to hide your light beneath a bushel Olive,' Joan coaxed, 'you are obviously very talented.'

'Well I did teach piano once. I'm just not good at getting to know people,' Olive admitted.

'But people here would like to know you and some have tried I'm told,' Joan reasoned. 'When you didn't follow up much on invitations they pulled back to give you time.'

'I did want to be part of the village and I did try to make an effort, but I have a knack of calling at the wrong time you see,' Olive explained, 'I went to one house and they were all crying because their dog had just died. Then, when I called to another house a relative had just arrived home in a taxi from the States. My timing is disastrous and I feel I'm intruding.'

Joan was trying hard not to smile. 'Olive, I'm sorry for seeing the funny side, and of course it's not funny that the Duggans' dog died but you're too inhibited. The people in this village would expect you to cry with them, or celebrate with them when a taxi brings their brother home. You just go on in instead of backing out again, if no-one takes special notice of you it's because you're accepted. Now, how about the piano?'

'Well, maybe,' Olive wavered.

'Oh come on Olive,' Joan urged, 'time's up.'

'I'll do it!' Olive suddenly decided.

'I'm glad you said that because there's more,' Joan winced.

Olive smiled knowingly, 'You haven't got a piano?'

'Would you mind if we met here until we get one, and somewhere to practice?' Joan asked hopefully. 'The men have decided to build a currach. It is their boathouse, but they need an awful lot of room and they make an awful lot of noise. They don't mind us having our Thursday meetings in the top half but I can't see them handing the place over for a second evening in the week. Imagine us singing at one end while they bash and hammer at the other.'

'I'd be delighted,' Olive assured her, and she was. 'We can meet in the house certainly, but if we need more space, what about the barn out the back? It's got a big ground floor that Ronnie was converting as a mini gym, all we have to do is move the piano over.'

'And we'd be independent!' Joan marvelled.

'There's lino laid and electricity installed, and we could do it up a bit more,' Olive added.

'Olive you're a gem!' Joan exclaimed. 'This certainly has been a productive day.'

More productive than Joan would ever know, Olive smiled inwardly. Her visit and the warmth of her friendship had made it the day Olive had yearned for, and after this her life wouldn't have to be lonely anymore. She only had to believe her own worth and trust her own decisions. Tomorrow was her day, and lilac was definitely her colour.

Freda Cave is a grandmother and lives in Mourne in Co. Down with her husband. They both like wildlife and nature, and she likes to go rambling with their two dogs. She says she 'writes quietly as a hobby.' She initially had three stories published in Woman's Way *over the years and she returned to more regular writing after her husband became ill in 2013 with great success, having almost 20 stories published in* Ireland's Own *magazine.*